Enhancing Nonsymbolic Communication Interactions among Learners with Severe Disabilities

Enhancing Nonsymbolic Communication Interactions among Learners with Severe Disabilities

by

Ellin Siegel-Causey, Ph.D.
and
Doug Guess, Ed.D.

Special Education Department
University of Kansas
Lawrence

with invited contributors

·P·A·U·L·H·
BROOKES
PUBLISHING Co

Baltimore • London • Toronto • Sydney

Paul H. Brookes Publishing Co.
Post Office Box 10624
Baltimore, Maryland 21285-0624

This work has been funded at least in part with Federal funds from the U.S.
Department of Education under Contract Number 300-83-0237. The content of
this publication does not necessarily reflect the views or policies of the U.S.
Department of Education nor does mention of trade names, commercial prod-
ucts, or organizations imply endorsement by the U.S. Government.

Typeset by Brushwood Graphics, Inc., Baltimore, Maryland.
Manufactured in the United States of America by
Thomson-Shore, Inc., Dexter, Michigan.

Library of Congress Cataloging in Publication Data

Enhancing nonsymbolic communication interactions among learners with severe
  disabilities / by Ellin Siegel-Causey and Doug Guess; with invited contributors.
    p.   cm.
  Bibliography: p.
  Includes index.
  ISBN 1-55766-019-0
    1. Mentally handicapped children—Means of communication. 2. Mentally
handicapped children—Education. I. Guess, Doug.
RJ506.M4S75   1989   89-30385
618.92′855—dc 19   CIP

Contents

Contributors

Christy Battle, M.S.
Callier Center for Communication Disorders
1966 Inwood Road
Dallas, Texas 75235

Barbara Ernst, B.S.
1629 North 52nd Street
Seattle, Washington 98103

Doug Guess, Ed.D.
Special Education Department
University of Kansas
3150 Haworth Hall
Lawrence, Kansas 66045

Ellin Siegel-Causey, Ph.D.
Special Education Department
University of Kansas
3150 Haworth Hall
Lawrence, Kansas 66045

Robert Stillman, Ph.D.
Callier Center for Communication Disorders
1966 Inwood Road
Dallas, Texas 75235

Communication is the most efficient and organized method we have for transmitting information about ourselves, our world, and others. Relaying this information is necessary for all people to achieve a level of independence and to function effectively in the environment. Communication is essential to growth, enabling people to develop a degree of control and autonomy in their daily lives.

This goal of independence must be considered in all levels of communication and language intervention. Those individuals possessing a nonsymbolic repertoire must be allowed to experience effective control in their interactions in the environment. The quality of their nonsymbolic repertoire needs to incorporate a variety of understandable, functional messages. The intended receivers must be sensitive and responsive to these unconventional signals so that effective exchanges can occur.

e.s.-c.
b.e.

Acknowledgments

This book represents the culmination of a graduate project I began during my doctoral training at the University of Kansas. I extend my thanks to Christy Battle, June Downing, Barbara Ernst, Doug Guess, and Robert Stillman who each contributed to the actual concepts and writing.

Also, thanks to the students at the University of Kansas and colleagues in the field who reviewed this book and provided evaluative feedback, especially Christy Battle, Michael Bullis, June Downing, Linda Dyer, Lori Goetz, James Halle, Susan Brody Hasazi, Jeanne Johnson, Linda McCormick, Pat Mirenda, Charles (Cap) Peck, Caryn Robbins-Studyvin, Charity Rowland, Dick Sobsey, Robert Stillman, and Liz Vogt.

Special thanks go to Karin Soper and Sue Johnson for their countless hours of editing and typing. I appreciate all of you!

Ellin Siegel-Causey, Ph.D.
Special Education Department
University of Kansas

We dedicate this book to the many insightful and thoughtful teachers and therapists of children and youth with profound handicaps who have known all along the importance of sensitive, child-centered interactions in educational programs.

Preface

The task of developing communication and interactional skills among students with severe and multiple handicaps who do not possess a formal symbolic system has challenged educators for many years—likely since the inception of that area of special education devoted to those children and youth who experience the most profound intellectual, sensory, and motor impairments. For the most part, previous educational efforts and programs have concentrated primarily on those students who have responded, at least in part, to instructional procedures designed to teach or enhance speech, signing, or other conventional symbolic modes of expression. We now recognize that these past techniques and programs have not been effective with a significant number of students who, for whatever reason, have failed to respond to existing approaches and orientations. Equally important, we have come to understand that past efforts might well have "missed the mark" in both interpreting the communication needs of students with the most profoundly handicapping conditions, and in applying that which was considered to be state-of-the-art practices. This book is offered as an initial step in redirecting our efforts to more completely understand and adequately program for the communication and interactional needs and behaviors of those children and youth who have not yet reached the level of what most adults would identify as conventional modes of expression.

For those persons who are looking for a "cookbook" approach to instruction, this book is likely to be disappointing. Instead, a more general, and for many, a quite different orientation for better understanding and developing the functional communication repertoires among students with severe and profound language delays can be found. There are several reasons for this.

First, the orientation of the approach in this book assumes that children and youth with the most handicapping conditions do indeed communicate; however, this communication is achieved in a variety of ways that are not readily observed or even acknowledged by many attending adults. This assumption implies that teachers, therapists, and caregivers must become more sensitive in both observing and responding to often fleeting, subtle, and yet important nuances of behavior that are used by these children and youth to "communicate" with others. Indeed, the students, and their accompanying behaviors are brought back to the center of the educational process, replacing in many respects the preprogrammed, adult-centered agendas that now reflect much of our educational programming in the severely multiply handicapped area of special education. The student is thus perceived as an active, dynamic participant in the educational process; one who, if carefully observed, will be found to possess many latent but positive behaviors and skills that can be further expanded and developed by teachers and caregivers.

The second major aspect of the orientation for this book acknowledges then, the importance of teacher and caregiver interactional skills that go far beyond written programs, data sheets, and other prescribed formulas for merely eliciting student responses to a usually small number of predetermined communication goals and objectives. Users of this resource must reflect, in great part, the combined skills of a teacher, clinician, problem-solver, and innovator—a technician will not suffice. The book does provide for the teacher and caregiver some quite explicit observational and interactional skills that are needed to accelerate the communication development of children and youth with nonsymbolic forms of expression. The book does not, however, rely on a sequential display of skill achievements that can be charted vertically by the teacher or caregiver. It recognizes, rather, the extreme complexity of communication development among children and youth with severe and profound handicaps, and the often uneven and yet important interactions between various skills that are combined, in often unique ways, to produce the types of behavior that are eventually perceived as a formal language system.

It is important to note that while the organization and content in this book is still undergoing experimental analysis with students who have severely and profoundly handicapping conditions and their teachers and caregivers, the basic concepts and principles that underlie this resource have been derived from extensive research and theory in both normal infant and child development and from extant literature in the areas of exceptionality and communication development. For this reason, the reader is referred to the chapter by Siegel-Causey, Ernst, and Guess (1989) for a more complete literature review and analysis of the concepts that provide the basis for the content and orientation of this book.

The sincere hope of the authors is that this book will provide for the field a positive contribution to the education of students with profound, severe, and multiply handicapping conditions; and by so doing, lay the foundation for further research and personnel training endeavors that reflect more accurately the immense needs of these students and, ultimately, the promise of a better future.

Doug Guess, Ed.D.
Special Education Department
University of Kansas

REFERENCE

Siegel-Causey, E., Ernst, B., & Guess, D. (1989). Nonsymbolic communication in early interactional processes and implications for intervention. In M. Bullis (Ed.), *Communication development in young children with deaf-blindness: Literature Review IV.* Monmouth, OR: Deaf-Blind Communication Skills Center.

Enhancing Nonsymbolic Communication Interactions among Learners with Severe Disabilities

INTRODUCTION TO NONSYMBOLIC COMMUNICATION

*Robert Stillman and
Ellin Siegel-Causey*

Effective communicative exchanges between individuals with severe, multiple disabilities and service providers are essential for mutual understanding and quality interactions. Many individuals with severe, multiple disabilities do not use conventional *symbolic*[1] systems (e.g., speaking, writing) to communicate with others. Therefore, it is essential that intervention efforts focus on facilitating and responding to the existing *nonsymbolic* (e.g., gestures, vocal sounds, eye contact, body movements, facial expressions) abilities of each individual.[2]

Communication is the process of exchanging information. It is the means by which people affect each other's thoughts and actions. For most people, communication is so effortless that it is rarely given much thought. Only when a person is encountered who does not understand typical communications or whose communications are not readily understood by other individuals do people begin to appreciate the importance of this most fundamental interpersonal skill.

There are many purposes for communication and ways to achieve it. People communicate to elicit or change another person's behavior, to offer information and convey thoughts and feelings, and for the purely social reason of engaging in an interaction with someone. Most people, when they communicate, use spoken *language*. Spoken language is composed of a system of symbols (e.g., words), the use of which is governed by complex grammatical rules. Not all communication, however, relies on the use of symbol systems. Nonsymbolic forms of communication such as facial expressions, gestures, movements, postures, and touch are commonly observed and mutually understood in conversations between language users.

Many learners who have severe, multiple disabilities neither use nor understand the symbols and rules of language. To communicate with these learners, service providers must be able to recognize the learner's nonsymbolic communication and systematically use nonsymbolic communication to facilitate the learner's ability to understand. Instructional strategies have been developed to give service providers (e.g., educators, paraprofessionals, therapists) procedures for teaching numerous skills to individuals with severe disabilities. However, communication skills training with these persons continues to be problematic (Bullis, 1985, 1986, 1987, 1989; Donnellan, Mirenda, Mesaros, & Fassbender, 1984; Goetz & Sailor, 1988; Hammer, 1982; Musselwhite & St. Louis, 1988; Peck & Schuler, 1987; Reichle & Keogh, 1986; Schuler & Prizant, 1987; Stillman & Battle, 1986c).

If successful interactions are observed between service providers and learners who have severe, multiple disabilities, many instances of nonsymbolic communication may be seen. For example, the learner's cry communicates to the service provider to seek and relieve the source of discomfort. The learner's reach communicates to the service provider to bring the cup within grasping range. The learner's alternating glance between a toy and the service provider's hand communicates to the service provider to activate the toy. In each example, the learner's nonsymbolic communication has the effect of engaging the service provider in an interaction, and results in the learner's attainment of a desired goal.

Service providers also use nonsymbolic communication to engage learners in interactions and to achieve their own communicative goals. For example, the service provider may pause in a movement with the learner to elicit a communication to continue, tap the learner on the shoulder to gain attention, hold out two objects to offer the learner a choice, or make a twisting motion over a container to show the learner how to remove the lid. Nonsymbolic communication plays a key role in most interactions, especially with learners who do not use symbolic communication and whose clear understanding of language symbols cannot be assumed. For

---

[1]Words in italic are defined in the Glossary at the end of this book.

[2]The authors have chosen to use the term "nonsymbolic." The usage of "presymbolic" or "prelinguistic" was avoided because these terms present a connotation of the inevitable transition and development of symbolic communication. The authors recognize that some individuals with severe, multiple disabilities will not use symbols but will communicate in a nonsymbolic manner.

these learners, expanding their use of nonsymbolic communication helps them to acquire the means to influence others and to become more active participants in interactions. For service providers, the use of nonsymbolic communication helps them to convey information in a manner that is more readily detected and understood by the learner. It is not the authors' intent to diminish the importance of symbolic communication. Excessive emphasis on symbol acquisition, however, might prevent service providers from recognizing and taking advantage of the existing nonsymbolic communicative abilities of an individual.

Most service providers expect to observe and promote "*language*" in the clients and learners with which they work. Service providers typically use spoken language (i.e., symbolic system) to communicate; however, it might be problematic to adjust their *expressive* messages with individuals who have severe sensory, mental, and/or physical disabilities. Although service providers may recognize nonsymbolic communication as commonplace in their interactions, they might not be fully aware of the many forms of nonsymbolic communication to which they can respond and might not systematically use nonsymbolic communication to convey information and to enhance the learner's communicative skills.

This book presents an intervention approach that stresses the *reciprocal* nature of communication exchanges. This orientation emphasizes intervention at three levels:

1. **To enhance the service providers' perceptions and understanding of an individual's nonsymbolic repertoires**
2. **To enhance the use of nonsymbolic expressions by the learner with severe, multiple disabilities**
3. **To encourage service providers to use nonsymbolic communications as a means to enhance the exchange of information with learners**

Thus, this intervention approach recognizes that communication interactions are experienced mutually by the service provider and the learner, and that both individuals are reciprocally affected by each others's expressions during interactions.

OVERVIEW OF CONTENTS

To assist service providers to incorporate nonsymbolic communication in their activities, five instructional guidelines are used in this book:

1. Developing *nurturant* relationships
2. Enhancing *sensitivity* to nonsymbolic communication
3. Increasing *opportunities* for communication
4. *Sequencing* experiences in predictable order
5. Utilizing *movement* within natural interactions

Each instructional guideline focuses on strategies for enhancing the learner's communicative skills and increasing the effectiveness of communicative interactions. The guidelines emphasize communication because communication pervades all social and instructional activities. Whether the primary objective of an activity is to develop the learner's communicative abilities, teach *functional* skills, or encourage social behaviors, the ability of the learner and service provider to effectively communicate significantly affects the outcome of the intervention effort.

The five instructional guidelines with underlying theoretical and research support are presented in Section 2. These guidelines incorporate strategies for service providers to use to accommodate the unconventional or limited auditory, visual, motor, and vocal abilities of the individual who is nonsymbolic and who has severe disabilites. Throughout Section 2, examples of the instructional guidelines are given. In Section 3, the instructional guidelines are incorporated into descriptions of reciprocal dialogues of adult-learner interactions. The authors' reason for including the instructional guidelines is that the service provider and the learner will learn to utilize *receptive* and *expressive* nonsymbolic behaviors in an expanded, facilitory manner. The focus on expanding the use of nonsymbolic communication by both the service provider (e.g., educators, paraprofessionals, therapists) and the learner is intended to help both of them improve their communication skills.

Therefore, it is suggested in this book that service providers expand their personal use of nonsymbolic expressions combined with their symbolic expressions. The instructional guidelines provide examples of how service providers can combine their symbolic and nonsymbolic expressions. In addition, the book enables service providers to help learners with severe disabilities to enhance their communicative understanding (i.e., *reception*) of the nonsymbolic behaviors that others use and to expand their own use (i.e., *expression*) of nonsymbolic behaviors. An overview of this dual, reciprocal nature of expression and reception of communication is displayed in Figure 1.

The figure displays the learners' and service providers' use of nonsymbolic expression. Examples of these nonsymbolic expressions include: vocal (e.g., crying, grunting, laughing), affect (e.g., facial expressions), tactual (e.g., physical contact, affection), gestural (e.g., outstretched arms, head nod), physiological (e.g., drowsy, alert, asleep), body movement (e.g., leaning toward or away, mobility), and visual (e.g., gaze, attention). The service provider's symbolic expressions may include: verbal (e.g., talking), sign language (e.g., signing, "Want

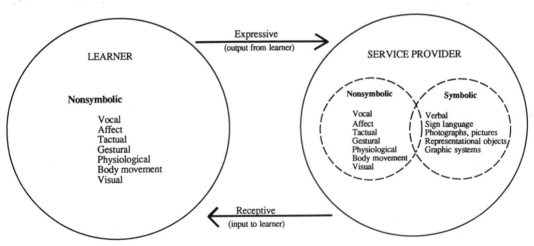

Figure 1.   Dual, reciprocal nature of communication interactions that involve nonsymbolic expressions from the learner and both nonsymbolic with symbolic expressions from the service provider.

NONSYMBOLIC	SYMBOLIC
Vocal—using sounds and utterances	Verbal—using words
Affect—displaying a feeling or emotion	Sign language—using system of hand and arm gestures
Tactual—using touch (stimulation of passive skin receptors and active manipulation and exploration)	Photographs and pictures—using visual representation or image
Body movement—general motion of body such as leaning, pulling away, or swaying	Representational objects—using miniature objects to depict real objects or activities; using portions of a real object to depict a real object or activity
Gestural—using movement of the limbs or body parts	
Physiological—displaying functions of body such as alertness or muscle tone	Graphic system—using a method of symbols (Blissymbolics, rebus pictures)
Visual—using sense of sight	

more?" or "Yes"), photographs/pictures (e.g., picture of learner, drawing of object), representational objects (e.g., toy chair to respresent learner's chair), and graphic systems (e.g., orthography, Blissymbols, rebus pictures). The overlapping of the nonsymbolic and symbolic circles in the figure depict the service provider's ability to express with nonsymbolic behaviors, symbolic behaviors, or nonsymbolic and symbolic behaviors simultaneously.

The remainder of Section I discusses the elements of the communicative process with specific references to interactions between service providers and learners with severe, multiple disabilities.

ELEMENTS OF THE COMMUNICATIVE PROCESS

Communication is a process of sharing: in recognition of each other's communicative expressions, in understanding the topics and purposes of each other's communication, and in the knowledge that communication is interpersonal and *reciprocal* (Rowland & Stremel-Campbell, 1987). Sharing in interactions between service providers and learners, however, cannot always be assumed. It is the role of the service provider, as the more competent communicator, to serve as the learner's guide and model in achieving a shared understanding of the methods and uses of communication.

Recognizing Nonsymbolic Communication

In considering elements of nonsymbolic communication, it is perhaps best to begin with the observable acts or behaviors that may serve a communicative function. Practically any behavior has the potential to be communicative. All that is required is that the behavior be detectable by the recipient, and distinguishable from the other stimuli to which both service provider and learner are continuously exposed. Some nonsymbolic communications are conventional, in the sense that most people would identify the behavior as communication. Pointing, smiling, a pat on the back, or a hand motion of "come here" are all conventional, nonsymbolic communications. Other nonsymbolic communications, however, may be less obviously communicative because they grow out of shared experiences or are recognizable only with regard to the context in which they appear. For example, a learner holding out a hand to initiate a hand-wiggling game may be recognizable only to the service provider who has previously played the game with the learner. The service provider holding up a napkin may signal lunch only because the learner has observed this action preceding lunch many times in the past.

Table 1 depicts communicative forms that may be used by service providers. To emphasize the many avenues for communicating, the examples are divided according to the sensory modality through which the learner receives the communication. Recognition of these modes of communication may assist service providers in recognizing and better utilizing these natural communicative abilities of all individuals that are present, regardless of impairments or lack of symbolic (e.g., expression) skills. In reviewing the examples, service providers may wish to consider which communicative methods they might use with particular learners to:

1. Gain attention
2. Elicit desired behaviors
3. Help the learner anticipate coming events or recall past events
4. Share information
5. Engage and maintain the learner in reciprocal interactions

Table 1. Forms of service providers' communicative expressions

Modality	Symbolic	Nonsymbolic
Auditory	Service provider speaks to learner	Service provider turns on music to indicate the start of physical therapy Service provider uses a nonspeech vocalization to attract the learner's attention
Visual	Service provider signs to learner	Service provider makes pointing movement to draw learner's attention to an object Service provider holds out spoon to see if learner is ready for a bit of food Service provider draws a picture with learner to indicate the next activity Service provider makes a twisting motion over the lid of a container to demonstrate to the learner how to open it Service provider makes an exaggerated movement to elicit learner's attention
Tactile	Service provider fingerspells in learner's hand	Service provider taps learner's hand to prompt the learner to pick up an object Service provider puts hands under the learner's arms and pauses to indicate that the learner is about to be picked up Service provider rubs learner's legs in a downward direction to request learner's assistance in pulling pants off Service provider ties bib on learner to indicate lunch
Kinesthetic	Service provider manipulates learner's hands through the "finish" sign to indicate that the activity is over	Service provider pauses while rocking with the learner to elicit a signal to continue Service provider manipulates the learner's hands through the start of pouring from a container to elicit the learner's participation
Olfactory		Service provider holds spoon near learner's nose to see if learner wants the particular food item

Table 2 lists nonsymbolic forms of communication that service providers should look for in the learners' behavior. The list is somewhat broader than for service providers, reflecting the range of communicative skills observed among learners. The list includes forms of communication that, like those of service providers, are typically used in a purposeful and goal-directed manner. These include reenactments (Schuler & Prizant, 1987), repetitions of actions that previously resulted in the learner's achievement of goals, or action that the learner has observed that others perform to achieve goals. Reenactments, because they are derived from the learner's individual experiences, may be unique to each particular learner. Others, however, reflect experiences common to many learners.

In addition to goal-directed communications, Table 2 includes behaviors that are communicative only in the sense that they tell the service provider something about the learner's emotional state, level of arousal, or attentiveness to external stimuli. A major task for service pro-

Table 2. Forms of learner nonsymbolic communications

Generalized movements and changes in muscle tone
Excitement in response to stimulation or in anticipation of an event
Squirms and resists physical contact
Changes in muscle tone in response to soothing touch or voice, in reaction to sudden stimuli, or in preparation to act

Vocalizations
Calls to attract or direct another's attention
Laughs or coos in response to pleasurable stimulation
Cries in reaction to discomfort

Facial expressions
Smiles in response to familiar person, object, or event
Grimaces in reaction to unpleasant or unexpected sensation

Orientation
Looks toward or points to person or object to seek or direct attention
Looks away from person or object to indicate disinterest or refusal
Looks toward suddenly appearing familiar or novel person, object, or event

Pause
Ceases moving in anticipation of coming event
Pauses to await service provider's instruction or to allow service provider to take turn

Touching, manipulating, or moving with another person
Holds or grabs another for comfort
Takes or directs another's hand to something
Manipulates service provider into position to start an activity or interactive "game"
Touches or pulls service provider to gain attention
Pushes away or lets go to terminate an interaction
Moves with or follows the movements of another person

Acting on objects and using objects to interact with others
Reaches toward, leans toward, touches, gets, picks up, activates, drops, or pushes away object to indicate interest or disinterest
Extends, touches, or places object to show to another or to request another's action
Holds out hands to prepare to receive object

Assuming positions and going to places
Holds up arms to be picked up, holds out hands to initiate "game," leans back on swing to be pushed
Stands by sink to request drink, goes to cabinet to request material stored there

Conventional gestures
Waves to greet
Nods to indicate assent or refusal

Depictive actions
Pantomimes throwing to indicate, "throw ball"
Sniffs to indicate smelling flowers
Makes sounds similar to those made by animals and objects to make reference to them
Draws picture to describe or request activity

Withdrawal
Pulls away or moves away to avoid interaction or activity
Curls up, lies on floor to avoid interaction or activity

Aggressive and self-injurious behavior
Hits, scratches, bites, or spits at service provider to protest action or in response to frustration
Throws or destroys objects to protest action or in response to frustration
Hits, bites, or otherwise harms self or threatens to harm self to protest action, in response to frustration, or in reaction to pain or discomfort

viders is to sort out the learner's behaviors that require a specific response from those that indicate the learner's readiness or willingness to interact. These, in turn, must be distinguished from the learner's random, reflexive, or self-stimulatory movements and vocalizations. In reviewing Table 2, service providers might consider:

1. Which forms they identify and respond to when interacting with particular learners
2. Which forms are used by particular learners to purposefully achieve desired goals and which are mainly indicators of the learners' emotional state
3. Which forms, if consistently encouraged and expanded, will enhance the learner's ability to successfully participate in social interactions

Tables 1 and 2 show that when considering nonsymbolic communications, the range of possible ways for both service provider and learner to communicate is almost unlimited. The burden on the service provider, however, is to select communicative forms that can be readily detected and attended to by individual learners and to be sensitive to the communicative potential of all of the learner's behaviors. It is also the responsibility of the service provider to be aware of the forms of communications to which the learner reliably responds and to systematically expand the learner's receptive abilities through the gradual introduction of new forms. It is also the service provider's responsibility to evaluate each learner's behavior as possible efforts to communicate, especially those that are object- or person-directed.

Understanding Nonsymbolic Communications

Recognizing nonsymbolic expressions is the starting point for effective communicative interactions. Accurate understanding, however, and appropriate response to these expressions is what determines the success of both the learner's and the service provider's communicative efforts.

Accurate understanding and appropriate response means that the purpose of the communication and the effect it has on the recipient are the same. The purpose of a communication refers to the communicator's goal (i.e., what the communicator expects will happen in response to the expression). The effect of a communication is how the recipient, in fact, responds to the communication. The following examples describe nonsymbolic communications that are successful because there is a match between the purpose of the communication and the effect that it has on the partner:

1. The service provider pauses in a movement familiar to the learner for the purpose of eliciting a communication to continue. The learner, recognizing that the familiar movement has been interrupted, directs an action toward the service provider for the purpose of reinitiating the movement. The service provider recognizes the learner's directed action as a communication to resume the movement and responds accordingly. The learner, then, rejoins the service provider in the movement.
2. The service provider places a cup on the learner's tray to communicate that it is snack time. The learner, as a result of previous similar experiences, recognizes that the cup means snack and pushes the cup to the service provider to communicate "wanting juice." The service provider pours the juice and holds the filled cup out to the learner to determine if the learner's communication (i.e., pushing the cup) actually meant, "want juice." The learner smiles and reaches for the cup. The service provider responds by assisting the learner to bring the cup to his or her mouth.
3. The learner reaches toward an object for the purpose of obtaining it. The service provider, recognizing the communicative purpose of the learner's action, extends a hand to the

learner. The learner, recognizing that the service provider's hand in this situation means "help in obtaining something," moves the service provider's hand toward the object. The service provider obtains the object and gives it to the learner.

When there is a discrepancy between the purpose of the communication and its actual effect on the recipient, the interaction proceeds less smoothly. There are several reasons why a discrepancy may occur: the recipient (e.g., service provider, learner) may fail to recognize an action as a communication, the particular communicative act may be unclear and open to several possible interpretations, or the recipient may not wish to respond or may be unable to respond in accordance with the purpose of the communication. The following are examples that illustrate a discrepancy between the purpose of a communication and its effect. The examples also describe the steps that the service provider might take in these situations to bring about correspondence between the purposes and effects of each other's communications:

1. The service provider places a cup on the learner's tray to communicate to the learner that it is snack time. The learner, not recognizing the service provider's action to be a communication, views the presence of the cup as an opportunity to play and begins manipulating and rolling the cup. The service provider sees that his or her communication did not have the desired effect; therefore, rather that stopping or admonishing the learner, the service provider tries a different form of nonsymbolic communication. This time the service provider holds the juice container in front of the student and begins making pouring motions. The learner recognizes the service provider's communication and extends the cup toward the juice container.

2. The learner, after finishing a particular favorite food, pushes his or her plate toward the service provider to communicate that he or she wants more of this food. The service provider, assuming that the learner's nonsymbolic communication means that he or she is finished, communicates to the learner that lunch is finished by placing the plate on the cart holding dirty dishes, and makes the "finished" sign. Because the learner's communication did not produce the expected effect, the learner becomes agitated. The service provider, recognizing from the learner's response that the purpose of the learner's original communication was misinterpreted, retrieves the plate and points in succession to each of the bowls containing food. The learner vocalizes when the service provider points to his or her favored food. The service provider then helps the learner serve a second helping.

3. After getting a drink at the water fountain, the learner repeatedly presses the service provider's hand on the bar of the water fountain to make the water spray. The service provider, not wishing to continue this perseverative activity, responds to the learner's communication to spray the water by wiggling the learner's hand. The learner, recognizing this new and interesting response to the actions, begins motioning to the service provider to continue this action. When the service provider determines that the learner has become involved in this new "game" and is distracted from the water fountain, he or she moves with the learner to a new activity.

These six examples of matched and descrepant exchanges demonstrate the importance of shared understanding of communications that are needed for effective and productive interactions to occur. For service providers to promote shared understanding, they must view nonsymbolic communicative interactions, not only from their own perspective, but also from the perspective of the learner. Service providers need to consider what the learner is likely to anticipate or to understand from each communication. The following are some factors that encourage the learner's shared understanding of the service provider's communications:

1. Topics about which the service provider communicates should be relevant to the learner's experiences and appropriate to his or her level of understanding. For many learners, this means focusing on topics related to present actions, objects, persons, and events, especially those that are presently intriguing to the learner.
2. Service providers should think of their nonsymbolic communications as a means of simplifying and clarifying communication, and use forms that relate in a concrete way to the information to be communicated. Pointing movements to direct the learner's attention, holding up or giving the learner objects used in an activity to indicate the start of the activity, and demonstrating an action to request that the learner do the same are examples of ways service providers may assist learners to understand the relationship between the communicative act and the purpose of the communication.

In promoting shared understanding, service providers must also be skilled at recognizing the learners' goals in communicating, and be prepared to assist learners in attaining their goals. Learners cannot assume that the purposes of their communications are shared unless they produce predictable responses. The following are some factors that encourage learners to understand that their communications are shared:

1. The service provider's immediate, appropriate, and consistent response to the learner's communications is the single most important way to indicate shared understanding. It is through consistent responses that learners acquire understanding of the value of communication. Even when a learner's communication must be rejected because it requests a perseverative activity or it cannot be appropriately responded to at that time, efforts should be made to acknowledge the communication and to offer the learner a positive alternative.
2. Efforts to encourage the learner to use more sophisticated or precise forms of communication should not unduly disrupt the flow of natural interactions. Demands on the learner to repeat communications, communicate another way, or communicate more clearly should be reserved for situations highly motivating to the learner so as to not reduce the learner's desire to communicate and the service provider's opportunity to demonstrate shared understanding.
3. Service providers should keep each other and the learner's family informed of the forms and purposes of the learner's communications. Learners begin to understand the conventional nature of communication when their communicative efforts bring about predictable responses from all of their social partners.

UNDERSTANDING THE RECIPROCAL AND
INTERPERSONAL NATURE OF NONSYMBOLIC COMMUNICATIVE INTERACTIONS

The previous sections described sharing in recognition and understanding of each other's communications. This section focuses on the structure and patterns of communicative interactions and the shared understanding of the reciprocal and interpersonal roles that each partner plays.

An interaction is really a sequence of communications—a dialogue between partners where each has the opportunity to communicate and each has the obligation to respond. *Reciprocity* refers to the partners' dual roles as both initiators and responders in communicative interactions. Assisting learners to participate in interactions as both successful initiators and responders is an important consideration for service providers. Often, service providers place the learner entirely in the role of responder by communicating a series of instructions or demands to which the learner must respond. Or, they place the learner in the role of initiator, passively awaiting learner actions to which the service provider can respond. Reciprocity is missing when one partner dominates the interaction and the other is placed purely in the role of responder.

It is easy to understand how interactions can come to be dominated by one partner. Service providers may feel that they have specific instructional objectives to achieve and may view the learner's role in the interaction as one of performing in accordance with these objectives. The learner's efforts to initiate communications about topics not directly related to the objectives of the activity may be seen as unproductive digressions. Service providers may also view the learner as unable or unwilling to communicate. They may feel forced to dominate the interaction in order to maintain the learner's involvement. Contrarily, service providers may be so anxious to be responsive to the learner that they concentrate only on seeking and responding to learner behaviors. Service providers may find themselves reacting primarily to the learner's affective states or endlessly repeating actions, often involving physical stimulation of the learner, in response to the learner's repeated demands.

To understand what makes interactions reciprocal, it may be useful to think of reciprocal interactions as "conversations." Conversations have several features:

1. They are interpersonal in the sense that both partners are jointly focused on a topic.
2. They have a give-and-take flow with each partner having the opportunity to lead and follow.
3. They are progressive in that the topic changes over the course of the interaction.
4. They are a means to interpersonal ends.

Interpersonal Nature of Communication

The pattern of reciprocal interactions is one of give-and-take with each partner having the opportunity to lead and follow. In considering ways to encourage reciprocal interactions, however, service providers should think of reciprocity not as a structure to impose on learners, but as an outcome of the learner's developing understanding of the interpersonal nature of communication. Communication is, after all, an interpersonal process. Affording learners the opportunity to both initiate and respond is important, but only one aspect of the interpersonal process. Attaining a sense of interpersonal sharing is the real goal. Introducing learners to communication as an interpersonal process means guiding them to understand that in interacting with others, they are engaged in joint pursuit of common goals. Reciprocity is then an outcome because each partner shares responsibility for achieving the goals. There is a tendency to sometimes overlook the interpersonal side of communication, and to reduce communication to a practical skill, interpersonal only in that it happens to involve another person.

This emphasis on the practical side of communication is seen in assessment, in goals set for learners, and in the intervention strategies that service providers employ that typically focus on when the learner communicates, and what forms of communication the learner uses and understands. Communication, however, can be almost impersonal rather than interpersonal until learners begin to recognize that it is their engagement with another person, not just their actions that produce predictable effects.

Building Trust through Communication Introducing communication as an interpersonal skill is a process of building trust. For learners, trust emerges from a sense of familiarity with the actions of others, with how others respond to their actions, with the structure and sequence of events that they experience with others, and with how they and their partners together achieve goals and cause things to happen. Service providers must nurture the learner's trust in others through their consistency in actions and responsiveness to the learner's nonsymbolic communications. This trust can be further enhanced by providing opportunities for the learner to practice interactive skills, and by setting up circumstances so that through mutual involvement, certain desired goals are achieved and interesting exchanges occur.

SUMMARY

The guidelines presented in Sections 2 and 3 of this book are intended to encourage service providers to respond to the learner's nonsymbolic behaviors by observing, inferring intent, and responding in accordance with the learner's apparent goal in communicating. The goal is for individuals to learn the value of their unique repertoire of nonsymbolic behaviors by eliciting specific behaviors from other people. To assist learners to become more active participants in communicative interactions, the service provider may need to learn to display an awareness of the learner's nonsymbolic behaviors, and respond contingently in a meaningful manner within the context of each interaction. These behaviors should be viewed as the service provider's initial steps in eliciting the learner's attention and engaging him or her in interactions. This initial emphasis is intended to help learners discover that human partners are positive, rewarding people to interact with, and to learn that social interactions and the exchange of information can occur between themselves and others in a variety of social contexts.

This book provides a theoretical orientation and philosophy through the use of five instructional guidelines rather than a sequential, hierarchical step-by-step approach for delivering instruction. These guidelines (provide nurturance, enhance sensitivity, sequence experience, increase opportunities, and utilize movement) should be implemented as a total approach to interacting and relating to learners in all settings. The instructional guidelines described in this book are aimed at increasing service providers' nonsymbolic behaviors in interactions with individuals with disabilities. The assumption is that intervention should focus on the service providers in order for it to have a positive effect on the dynamic nature of nonsymbolic communicative exchanges and to enhance the nonsymbolic skills of the individual with disabilities.

All communicative interventions suggested in this book should:

1. Utilize *natural* context social interactions that are part of a daily schedule for a specific individual
2. Utilize materials that are age-appropriate, functional, and meaningful for the individual
3. Utilize functional settings with nondisabled peers
4. Compensate for auditory and visual loss through alternative sensory input (e.g., tactile, kinesthetic, olfactory, vibratory) (Siegel-Causey & Downing, 1987)

Interactions with a partner who uses only nonsymbolic communication modes require the listener (e.g., service provider, peer) to interpret or assign meaning to the message and then respond in a communicative manner. Ineffective interaction (e.g., a breakdown in communication) occurs frequently when a service provider or caregiver fails to recognize and consistently respond to the nonsymbolic expressions of a person with disabilities. When there is a breakdown of communication, the proper focus of intervention efforts is enhancing the receptive and expressive abilities of both participants within the "interactive processes," rather than on simply altering the limited repertoire of the individual with disabilities.

Social interactions play a significant role in communication development (Bates, Benigni, Bretherton, Camaioni, & Volterra, 1979; Bruner, 1975; Halliday, 1975). Intervention should occur frequently during dynamic and meaningful exchanges, and may require considerable effort on the part of the service provider. Intervention must focus on developing the service provider's personal skills that accommodate the unconventional or limited auditory, visual, motor, and vocal displays of the individual who is nonsymbolic.

Section 2 provides an overview of the five instructional guidelines with a review of the theoretical and research support for them. The instructional guidelines described in Section 2, and exemplified throughout the dialogues in Section 3, are designed to foster the learner's understanding of the interpersonal nature of communication and to encourage active participation in reciprocal communicative exchanges. The guidelines focus on strategies for establishing, nurturing, and trusting relationships, and on nonsymbolic communication, including individual and joint movements as the means by which interpersonal relationships, skills, and desire to communicate are established.

THEORETICAL ORIENTATION AND RESEARCH IN NONSYMBOLIC DEVELOPMENT

Ellin Siegel-Causey and Barbara Ernst

Implementation Considerations

This section provides a review of relevant literature found in infant communication theory and research and special education theory and research. These two sources provided the foundation for determining the content and suggested implementation of the five instructional guidelines that are the basis of this curriculum. The support for the use of the guidelines is derived from literature that verifies the components of the guidelines and is primarily based from extensive literature reviews that have been conducted for the past 4 years (Siegel-Causey, Ernst, & Guess, 1987, 1989; Siegel-Causey & Guess, 1985; Siegel-Causey, Sims, Ernst, & Guess, 1985, 1986, 1987, 1989).

The information compiled from the literature reviews on the nonsymbolic stage of development is particularly relevant to the communicative level of children with severe disabilities because many of these children function at a developmental stage that is very similar to the nonsymbolic communicative level of nondisabled infants. Both learners with severe disabilities or dual sensory impairments and infants without disabilities functioning at a nonsymbolic communicative level rely heavily on gestural, vocal, and tactual related means to communicate their needs.

There is increasing interest in the study of the social interaction process that can be observed in the caregiver-infant relationship, particularly in its relationship to the development of communication skills. Certain caregiving behaviors have been observed to promote the communication process and have been incorporated into specific intervention programs for children with disabilities (Klein & Briggs, 1987). Additionally, recent advances in the understanding of the nature of nonsymbolic communication in caregiver-infant interactions has provided a basis for more effective strategies for facilitating such communication in intervention programs with learners who have severe disabilities (Rowland & Stremel-Campbell, 1987; Stremel-Campbell & Rowland, 1987). Thus, the study of nonsymbolic interactions between infant and caregiver can provide important information that is relevant to nonsymbolic communication facilitation for the individual who is deaf-blind or experiencing severe disabilities.

There are two components of this curriculum guide that should be considered during all communication instruction. These components are natural context and functionality.

USING NATURAL CONTEXT IN COMMUNICATION INTERVENTION

The natural context of everyday life sets the stage for interactions providing many opportunities and reasons to communicate. Early communicative exchanges between the caregiver and the normally functioning infant occur in the natural context of the day as an indirect consequence of the infant's care and protection (Newson, 1977). Daily activities such as diapering, feeding, and bathing provide many natural opportunities for interactive exchanges to evolve between the infant and his or her caregiver. These daily activities provide an excellent opportunity for the caregiver to teach communication skills indirectly in a relaxed and emotionally supportive environment. Identifying and drawing from these quality learning situations found in the natural home environment of early caregiver-infant interactions may provide valuable insight into related intervention for young children with severe disabilities or deaf-blindness.

Natural contexts occur in any daily setting—educational, leisure, domestic, or vocational—providing a potentially continuous learning environment for the individual with severe disabilities. Additionally, the people involved in the natural environment (e.g., family, paraprofessionals, teachers) are an integral part of the individual's life and are, therefore, familiar and knowledgeable about the individual with severe disabilities. Caregivers and siblings, who are a significant part of the individual's natural home environment, can be encouraged to participate in communication facilitation, thereby increasing the occurrence of natural reciprocal social interactions. When nonhandicapped siblings become involved in the intervention process, the siblings with disabilities show an increase in the level of initiations and responses, and also display a greater ability to generalize newly acquired skills to other settings (James & Egel, 1986). The familiarity of the family can create a comfortable, relaxed atmosphere for the individual that encourages communicative interactions.

It is important to remember that service providers, over time, assume similar roles to the caregivers in the immediate family. As they become an integral part of the individual's natural environment, their interactions with that individual contain similar characteristics to the individual's caregivers in the home environment. They also establish nurturant, reciprocal roles with individual learners within their programs in the educational environment. The daily caregiving roles such as attending to physical needs, responding to nonsymbolic requests, and participating in social interchanges, occur between the adult and individual in home and in educational settings. Therefore, utilizing all components of the natural environment that enhance the communicative process should be encouraged in order to optimize the development of the individual with severe disabilities and to foster more competent behavior.

Natural Context in Instructional Settings

Communication training can be incorporated into educational and therapeutic programs by capitalizing on the spontaneous interactions that occur within a natural context. Using the naturally occurring opportunities of daily life provides a "common sense" framework that can be used to address communicative behaviors that have tended to occur in isolated, instructional rooms and areas within schools. In many instructional settings, speech-language clinicians, occupational therapists, and physical therapists have had their individual period of time to work on specific skills that may not be used by the child in any other environment. In fact, rarely do these skills, mastered during systematic, structured settings, appear appropriately in a child's spontaneous behavior in natural settings (Anderson & Spradlin, 1980; Liberty, Haring, & Martin, 1981; Warren & Rogers-Warren, 1985; Writer, 1987).

A variety of skills can be targeted within the learner's day by taking advantage of existing activities and interactions (Gaylord-Ross, Stremel-Campbell, & Storey, 1986). Learning may be enhanced when instruction occurs in the actual place where the skill is needed and involves the materials used in that setting. For example, a physical therapist can work in the classroom and accompany the learner during daily routines, such as preparing for recess (e.g., moving to the coat area, putting on a coat, going outside, participating with the child at recess). The physical therapist can be incorporating therapy goals such as weight shifting, balance, and bilateral

hand use within the context of these natural events. An added benefit is that the physical therapist can also incorporate natural communication opportunities as the therapy session unfolds
in a natural manner.

Intervention situations that are arranged precisely for the purpose of teaching specific
communication skills may lose some of the child's natural interest and spontaneity. These artifi-
cial teaching situations may result in a parroting of communicative behaviors that may be inappropriate or rarely used in the individual's daily life. In addition, the adult may be overly concerned with a specific response in the structured training session, inhibiting the individual's
other spontaneous communicative demonstrations. In fact, it has been found that instructional
staff generally respond at extremely low rates to behavior that is initiated during a formal instruction period by individuals with severe handicaps (Houghton, Bronicki, & Guess, 1987).
Shifting instruction away from the isolated and tightly controlled session, toward the use of an
environment with naturally occurring cues, removes the emphasis from a direct training mode
and may decrease adult directiveness and prompting.

Promoting a Natural Context in Schools

Instructional personnel in school settings can encourage natural, spontaneous communicative
opportunities that should be developed in the structured classroom. Essentially, school is a
natural environment where the learner spends 6 hours a day. The use of spontaneous social
interactions outside of the carefully programmed instructional schedule can be both practical
and immediately relevant to the individual with severe handicaps. Although the school setting
is restricted to the constraints of a predetermined schedule and structured environment, materials and activities can be arranged in a way to prompt occasions for communicative interactions to occur in an "ordinary, everyday" manner.

Everyday surroundings can be considered useful to facilitate communication during recess, lunch, vocational, and recreational periods and may be helpful in promoting other skills.
These activities may occur in an integrated setting with nondisabled learners, thus providing
more communicative possibilities.

Example of Natural Context in an Integrated School Setting

Johnny, who experiences severe multiple handicaps, is going into the community with his classroom and another classroom of students without disabilities. The purpose of the activity is to collect
leaves for a fall art project. During their browsing through a neighboring field, Johnny approaches
Anthony, a boy without disabilities, reaching toward him, vocalizing, and displaying a large leaf he
has just found. Anthony looks surprised and says, "Wow, Johnny, where'd you get that one?" Johnny
smiles broadly and looks around toward a big tree, nodding and moving his body excitedly . Anthony and Johnny walk to the tree with the big leaves, and together begin scouting around for more
leaves.

Spontaneous occurrences during any school activity may be used to incorporate a communicative skill better than trying to capture the individual's attention by using a predetermined, directive strategy. Additionally, the individual may be more motivated and interested
because the instruction is directly related to an ongoing, meaningful activity. Capitalizing on
these naturally occurring opportunities to promote communication is useful in facilitating the
individual's interactive competence. An incidental teaching opportunity or naturally occurring
opportunity can arise each time the student is in the presence of another person, and the
learner emits a behavior on which that person can elaborate. Using such natural occurrences as
a learning tool promotes a nonintrusive teaching role for the service provider to optimize the
learner's development and to foster more competent behavior (Dunst et al., 1987).

The natural environment supplies a number of different settings that may be used to encourage a child who is learning a new communicative skill. For example, if Billy is learning to express that he wants more, he may discover that by reaching, vocalizing, and pointing at the object of desire, he may evoke a helpful response from others. The teacher can indirectly prompt the use of this new skill in a number of natural settings.

Example of Using Natural Setting

During snack time, the teacher may pour half a glass of juice to give Billy an opportunity to ask for more. Billy may immediately vocalize or point at the empty cup. During a play session, the teacher may watch Billy play with a new wind-up toy and not respond immediately when the toy has stopped moving. She may wait for Billy to motion to her and express his desire for the toy to go again. At recess, when the teacher is pushing Billy in a swing, she can begin to push someone else and wait until Billy's swing comes to a stop, or until he calls out to her to start his swing again.

Ideally, communicative skills can be practiced in all settings during the day regardless of the scheduled activity. Opportunities to learn appropriate skills and communication strategies can be expanded to vocational, recreational, and other community settings. If individuals with severe disabilities enjoy these experiences they may have further incentive to interact and to learn new skills.

In summary, it is important to integrate natural, everyday events into communication training programs for the child with severe disabilities. Spontaneous communication exchanges can occur across a variety of settings and may greatly enhance the individual's communication skills. By being aware of the importance of a noninstructional atmosphere in the context of daily activities, more meaningful and appropriate interactions may arise.

INCORPORATING FUNCTIONALITY INTO COMMUNICATION INTERVENTION

It is important to remember that the goal of all intervention programs is to prepare individuals to function more effectively and independently. Behaviors that are targeted should be relevant to current living or school settings, incorporating a natural, common-sense approach (Mulligan, Guess, Holvoet, & Brown, 1980). Individuals with severe disabilities who may have difficulty in generalizing skills across different domains benefit from learning functional skills in natural contexts. Creating a learning situation that is directly applicable to the individual's daily life may promote communicative learning that is extremely practical for the individual with severe disabilities (Halle, 1982; Mulligan et al., 1980).

Taking Advantage of Communicative Opportunities

Relevant and practical skills can be taught to the learner with severe handicaps by taking advantage of existing activities and interactions in the learner's day. For example, communicative opportunities can be incorporated into the learning of functional skills such as self care and other relevant activities. Using regularly recurring events of daily life provides a familiar framework in which to address functional communicative behaviors. When skills are programmed for daily use, there may be a natural propensity for the learner to retain the skills. "Forgetting is generally a sign of disuse or irrelevancy" (Touchette & Schwartz, 1975, p. 12). Appropriate communication strategies will be relevant to the individuals' repertoire and for the world in which they actually function.

Functionality, as applied to communication, is based on the individual's communication expressions that can be immediately usable. Selection of functional nonsymbolic skills must be based on the individual's needs and characteristics, and the characteristics of the social and physical environments. The functionality of the targeted nonsymbolic skill should be analyzed by the response of the persons in the interactions and by the physical reactions in the environment. Kaiser, Alpert, and Warren (1987) suggest three steps to increase functional communication training:

1. Select forms that are known to be functional in particular settings that are frequented by the child. This requires "noting the type of interactions they engage in and the communication required to participate in those interactions" (Kaiser et al., 1987, p. 249).
2. Teach the child to use the forms selected in a functional manner by also training specific intentions. This requires considering opportunities for displaying intentions such as greeting, making choices, or requesting.
3. Respond to the child's forms in a functional manner. By doing this, meaning is derived from the consequence of the attempted communication. This may require adults to be "responsive to a student's emerging communication skills" (Kaiser et al., 1987, p. 249) and means that the child's expressions are attended and responded to by the service provider.

The home and school environment provide many occasions to incorporate a functional approach into communication intervention. For example, in both settings, instances occur frequently where the child may want to request something.

Example of Incorporating Functionality

At home, Jim finds that his towel is not hanging in its usual place. He goes to his mother and vocalizing to her, pulls her arm toward the cupboard with the towels.

At school, Jim may need help getting a box of crayons off of the shelf. He looks expectantly at the paraprofessional, and grabs her hand. The paraprofessional looks at him and waits. He vocalizes and brings her hand toward the box.

When items that children need or desire are not constantly replenished or supplied before they can ask for them, many occasions arise naturally for individuals to communicate their needs and desires for practical or functional reasons.

Natural Motivation for Communication

Individuals have a natural motivation to increase communication attempts when they observe that their behaviors can have a direct effect on the immediate environment. For a child who is learning what communication can do, receiving a specifically desired and requested object can be a very satisfying reward. The every day setting is ideal for this experience since the environment (e.g., home, school, outdoors) is full of objects that may be interesting to individuals. Strategies that incorporate this response-specific aspect, enabling individuals to observe direct cause and effect, will promote the individual's awareness of the usefulness of communication. Communicative behaviors are more readily learned and retained if this high motivational factor is present. Through the integration of functionality, individuals with severe disabilities may come to find that communication is a useful tool that can help them in their daily life.

Example of Using the Natural Appeal of the Environment

Isaac, a 12-month-old child with mental retardation and mild cerebral palsy, sees a bright colored ball roll under the sofa after the dog drops it. He motions toward the sofa, and attempts to crawl while he is grunting and struggling, intent on getting the ball. His father, seeing his interest says, "Do you want this, Isaac?" and reaches under the sofa to pull out the ball. Isaac sits up, wide-eyed, and reaches for the ball. "Are you sure you want it?," his father teases. Isaac reaches and smiles as he attempts to grab the ball. "Ok, ok, here it is." His father smiles broadly and places the ball in Isaac's hands.

Communicative opportunities can be extended into many natural contexts of the day (e.g., eating, toileting, bathing, dressing) so that functional skills are learned that are also appropriate to the individual's daily environment (Kent-Udolf, 1984). An environment that supports spontaneous individual involvement and includes incidental teaching interactions will facilitate learning and promote the use of newly learned behaviors across different domains (Halle, 1985). The emphasis on learning in a functional and natural environment strengthens the important relationship of content and context in intervention programs.

In the following section, five instructional guidelines will be introduced that are designed to be used in a home or educational setting while incorporating the concepts of natural environment and functionality. When both dimensions are considered together the probability of the intervention being successful is enhanced considerably.

Instructional Guidelines

T his part provides a review of each of the five instructional guidelines:

Developing nurturance
Enhancing sensitivity
Increasing opportunities
Sequencing experiences
Utilizing movement

These guidelines should not be used in a sequential manner. The service provider is expected to incorporate the relevant components of the five guidelines during any individual communicative interaction. Figure 2 displays the interrelated nature of the five guidelines that form the overall philosophical orientation of the curriculum. Figure 3 displays the specific intervention approaches of each of the five instructional guidelines.

The following review provides the reader with support from literature on infant communication development and from literature in special education as the basis for utilizing the instructional guidelines. Included are descriptions of each guideline and examples of interactions that incorporate components of these guidelines.

DEVELOPING NURTURANCE

Nurturance: Nurturance provides a supportive atmosphere through the development of a warm and trusting relationship.

Role in communication: Nurturance helps to create a positive relationship that promotes interest in communicative interactions and enhances a willingness to participate in social exchanges.

Role in caregiver-infant literature: The nurturance that caregivers provide infants establishes positive rapport and promotes the development of communication.

Role in nonsymbolic communication of individuals with severe disabilities: The service provider who creates a nurturant atmosphere for the individual with severe disabilities helps to establish the individual's interest in people and in communicative exchanges.

The basic concept of nurturance suggests a relationship between two persons founded on security, warmth, and mutual trust. Several authors have suggested that the nurturant relationship between infants and their primary caregivers supports and promotes early preverbal, nonsymbolic communication (Bruner, 1977; Newson, 1977; Odom, 1983; Schiefelbusch, 1984).

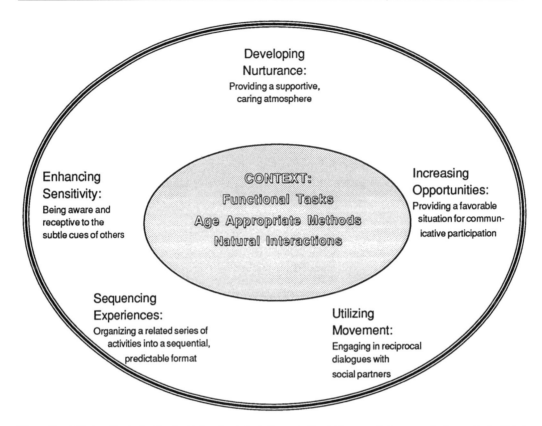

Figure 2. A display of five instructional guidelines in relation to the context in which nonsymbolic communication can be facilitated for learners with severe disabilities.

Adults who care for children in a nurturant manner by comforting, consoling, and encouraging them are providing a dependable framework for these children to develop relationships and enjoy interactions. When children are assured of the adult's availability and responsiveness, a secure base is provided and they can devote themselves more readily to exploring the world (Bates, Bretherton, Beeghly-Smith, & McNew, 1982; Kaye, 1982).

The nurturant caregiver establishes a sensitive relationship with the child that might aid the development of communication at a nonsymbolic level. When caregivers provide an atmosphere of warmth and security, and respond positively to the child's communicative behaviors, a relationship built on trust and confidence develops between them (Stillman & Battle, 1984; Writer, 1987). The nurturance that caregivers provide the child is essential in building a foundation for future communicative exchanges. Developing a nurturant relationship with individuals who have severe handicaps is also important for their future development. Individuals who receive warmth and concern from their service providers may naturally feel more trusting and comfortable within their environment. This, in turn, fosters a positive feeling for those individuals and may help to promote an interest in communicating with persons around them.

The development of a nurturant interactive pattern between caregiver and infant is crucial in the development of the child's future acquisition of communicative and cognitive skills. Studies have found that caregivers of normally functioning infants who were emotionally uninvolved with their infants consistently produced toddlers who scored significantly lower on cog-

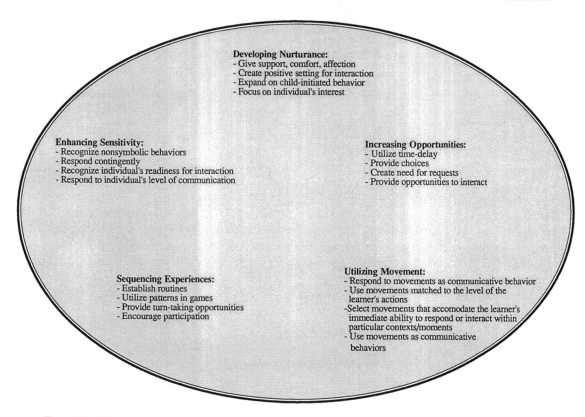

Figure 3.   Orientation to nonsymbolic communication facilitation: Specific instructional guidelines.

nitive, social, and linguistic tests (Field, 1983; Stern, 1974). Thus, there appears to be a positive correlation between caregiver attachment and the infant's eventual overall performance level.

The following section examines how the caregiver of the infant without disabilities exhibits nurturant behaviors, thereby developing a trusting, warm bond. It also considers how this feature may be relevant to the development of a nurturant atmosphere within the classroom for individuals with severe handicaps.

Caregivers' Nurturant Behaviors

The primary caregiver fosters nurturance by providing the infant with a secure environment and by developing a warm, affectionate bond. Caregivers will use many different gestural, vocal, and tactual behaviors to demonstrate their care and concern when interacting with infants. For example, the caregiver's eye gaze often follows the direction of the infant's eye gaze, so that, when the infant looks at the caregiver, eye contact is established. This reciprocal eye contact is seen as an important part of emotional bonding (Stern, 1977). Caregivers also use animated facial expressions, such as big smiles and wide eyes, to display their enjoyment and satisfaction with the infant. These expressions serve to capture the infant's attention, and instill positive feelings in both members of the *dyad*. In addition, caregivers use a special form of speech known as "motherese" or "baby talk." This unique speech pattern is the adult's way of adjusting speech to facilitate the infant's comprehension in an affectionate and nurturant manner. This style is characterized by an emotional warmth of intonation, combined with a simplification of speech forms for communicative clarity, and the use of affectionate words (Bakeman & Brown, 1977; Levin, Snow, & Lee, 1984; Walker, Levine, & Grasse, 1982).

Example of Nurturance

Jimmy's mother is swinging him in a hammock, playfully cooing, "Ooh, weee" in time with the motion of the hammock. As he swings near her, she leans over and kisses him quickly before the hammock swings back the other way. In a sing-song manner, she talks to him, saying, "Swinging, you are swinging, sweetheart" and caresses his head from time to time. Jimmy giggles and coos in delight, appreciating all the warmth and affection.

Caregivers' Nurturance in Daily Activities

There are continual opportunities for affectionate interchanges to occur during the first year of life as the bond between caregivers and infant develops. To a large extent, these exchanges occur as an indirect consequence of the physical care needed to keep an infant alive and well (Newson, 1977). The daily activities of diapering, feeding, and bathing provide many natural opportunities for warm social interaction to occur between infant and caregiver. While attending to the infant's physical needs, the caregiver has an excellent opportunity to express nurturant, caring behaviors.

Example of Caregiver Nurturance in Daily Activities

While changing Amy's diapers, Carol focuses on Amy's gaze and remains attentive to any noise or gesture that Amy makes. When Amy leans toward the bathroom shelf and vocalizes, Carol is quick to respond, bringing down a small stuffed animal that Amy enjoys.

The caregiver creates a supportive environment by responding sensitively and dependably to both the infant's social and physical needs. These repeated events that are necessary to daily life provide a familiar, reliable framework for the infant. During these times, infants become familiar with the caregiver's unique way of speaking to them, playing with them, and responding to them. The regularity experienced within these daily recurring activities promotes the infant's trust in the predictability of people in their environment. The infant is assured that the caregiver will be there and will provide whatever is needed.

Strategies Used to Develop Nurturance

Provide comfort, support, and affection
Create a positive setting for interactions
Expand on child-inititated behavior
Focus on individual's interest

Nurturance for the Child with Severe Disabilities

Children with disabilities and those with severe disabilities exhibit differences in early interactions that may affect the developing relationship and communicative development. The caregiver's early feelings of anxiety regarding the child's survival and/or development, the initial shock and continual adjustment, and the process of grieving, may contribute individually or collectively to the disruption of early communicative processes. The nurturant caregiver-infant relationship that is established normally in the first few weeks of life may be jeopardized by the caregiver who may be experiencing extreme loss, frustration, and emotional upheaval, re sulting possibly in withdrawal and unconscious or partial rejection of the child. The child may have complicated medical problems and require long hospitalization. Instead of experiencing warmth and nurturance, the caregiver may feel anxious and helpless. The infant born with disabilities may not readily achieve attachment to the caregiver, thereby inhibiting a mutually reinforcing relationship.

Furthermore, the caregiver's contact with the young child who is severely disabled is usually disrupted due to increased dependence on the professionals who provide intervention for the child. This allows less opportunity for the caregiver to establish and enhance a working communication system with the child (Kent-Udolf, 1984). Studies of interactions with infants with disabilities have found that caregivers exhibit less positive affective involvement during the first 2 years, and enjoy interactive exchanges less than caregivers of normally developing infants (Barnard, Bee, & Hammond, 1984; Crnic, Ragozin, Greenberg, Robinson, & Basham, 1983). Several studies have reported a progressive reduction in maternal interaction and emotional involvement after the first 2 years (Bricker & Carlson, 1981; Kogan, Tyler & Turner, 1974; Tyler & Kogan, 1977).

Many difficulties are inherent in the establishment of a nurturant relationship with individuals with severe handicaps. A stable, nurturant relationship that promotes trust and a feeling of security in the service provider is especially important for the individual with severe handicaps because it contributes significantly to the individual's interest in people and in future social interactions. When warm relationships are established, the individual with severe disabilities is more likely to interact with others. Emulating the nurturant, reciprocal relationship of the caregiver-infant dyad may enhance the service provider's communicative rapport with the individual.

Nurturance in the Educational Environment

A nurturant atmosphere in the educational environment may provide a learner with increased interest and motivation to participate in social exchanges. Service providers can incorporate nurturance in the classroom for learners with severe disabilities by demonstrating affection, displaying pleasure while interacting with the learner, positioning themselves to maintain eye/tactual contact, and using an affectionate tone of voice.

Service providers may also incorporate a nurturant atmosphere in the classroom by considering activities that bring the learner and adult into pleasurable interactions (Affleck, McGrade, McQueeney, & Allen, 1982). Individuals who experience enjoyable activities with a service provider tend to be more relaxed, happy, and receptive than children who feel tense and nervous due to an overdirective or controlling adult interaction. Typically, the caregiver of the child with severe handicaps is involved in daily teaching contexts, and thus, is more likely to exhibit directive behavior associated with the teaching role. During noninstructional situations, however, the service provider may be more sensitive to the learner's ongoing process of developing communicative skills and interests.

When interactions with an adult are not overly structured, or concerned only with "instruction," the communicative rapport may be spontaneous and enjoyable. Not having to focus always on the achievement of specific instructional goals may alleviate frustration for both learner and teacher. When the focus is not centered on whether the student can produce certain targeted behaviors, but rather on how the individual demonstrates his or her communicative competencies, appropriate supportive interchanges can occur (Dunst et al., 1987). The bond between learner and service provider can become stronger, and children may feel more comfortable and willing to interact when the learner has positive feelings associated with the adult and their time together.

Example of Nurturance Displayed in the Classroom for Learners with Severe, Multiple Disabilities

When it is time to go out to recess, the paraprofessionals need to make sure everyone is dressed properly in coats, gloves, and hats. Sarah, one paraprofessional, using an affectionate tone of voice, directs Ken, a student, toward the coat rack. She holds his hand and as they walk, they swing their arms back and forth slightly. While smiling at Ken, Sarah's tone of voice is warm as she says to him, "It's almost time for recess now, what do you need to do?" Ken returns the smile and looks delighted as he reaches for his coat. He obviously enjoys the attention Sarah pays him and uses his nonsymbolic behaviors (e.g., reaching, smiling) to communicate with her.

Focus on the Individual's Interest or Attention

Another way to expand on the feeling of nurturance in a school setting is to provide activities and materials in which the individual has shown an interest or to which he or she is currently attending. This strategy is observed frequently in the caregiver-infant dyad when caregivers unconsciously facilitate their interactions with the infant by making use of the infant's attention and other aspects of the immediate environment. Before infants intentionally communicate, caregivers promote interactions by searching for clues within the immediate context to decode the intent of their infant's cries. The literature on caregiver-infant interactions reveals maternal speech to be largely controlled by the concrete perceptual world of the young child. A large percent (65%–75%) of the mother's utterances to a 6-month-old refer to the infant's immediate surrounding (Collis & Schaffer, 1975; Snow, 1984). Additionally, most maternal vocalizations in a play setting refer to the infant's focus of attention or current activity. They may use the focus of the infant's immediate attention to build an appropriate learning situation.

Likewise, service providers can incorporate this extension of a nurturant relationship into the educational environment and, at the same time, create a more enjoyable learning situation. When considering activities to use to promote communication, selecting items that the individual seems to prefer may be met with more alertness and receptivity by the child. A growing body of evidence (Dunst et al., 1987) indicates that individuals with disabilities are more likely to display competent behavior if communication interactions are learner initiated and caregiver responses are related to the learner's ongoing behavior. Interactions can be initiated by focusing on the learner's immediate activity or interest. If the adult initiation is directly related to the individual's focus of attention, the individual may view the adult as a welcome participant, rather than as one who interrupts the activity. Expressing interest in an activity in which the individual is absorbed, omits the need to redirect attention and ensures interest. Teaching procedures that incorporate this strategy capitalizes on communication intervention that is not intrusive to the learner.

Example of Focusing on the Individual's Attention

Timmy has been distracted from the group play session and is struggling with his shoe, trying to pull it off. The physical therapist, seeing his lack of interest in the ongoing group activity, uses Timmy's current attention on the removal of his shoe to stress the same motor skills on which they had been working.

"Here, Timmy, if you untie your shoe by pulling on this shoe lace, it will be easier to pull the shoe off." Together, with her hand over his, they pull on the shoelace. Then, still with hands together, they pull on the heel of the shoe and it slides off. Timmy looks at her and smiles. "Now try it with the other shoe," she coaxes.

Timmy vocalizes as he begins to work on his other shoe. He has now forgotten the objects with which the other children are playing, but is engrossed in the task with his shoe. "Can you put your shoe back on, Timmy?" The therapist asks as she helps guide his hands as needed.

Replacing instructional or directive modes of interactions with more individual-oriented activities will promote a positive and nurturant atmosphere in the intervention program. Capitalizing on the learner's current attention encourages interactions that are directly related to his or her interest, making the educational environment a more pleasurable experience.

ENHANCING SENSITIVITY

Sensitivity: Being aware of and receptive to the subtle cues and behaviors of others is referred to as having sensitivity.

Role in communication: Interactions are facilitated when sensitivity is used to perceive and interpret the behaviors of others.

Role in caregiver-infant literature: Caregivers are sensitive to their infants' nonsymbolic behaviors and respond appropriately, thereby enhancing their communicative interactions.

Role in nonsymbolic communication of individuals with severe disabilities: Service providers can increase the quality of their communicative interactions with individuals with severe disabilities by becoming more sensitive to the unique communicative cues of the individual and responding in an enhanced manner.

Sensitivity plays an essential role in communication by facilitating a smooth and pleasant interchange. People use sensitivity in their daily interactions in order to accurately perceive and interpret the behaviors of others. A sensitive person is acutely aware of the attitudes and feelings of others, responds to their subtle cues, and is sympathetic to their needs and emotions. This section focuses on the role that sensitivity plays in the development of communication in the caregiver-infant dyad. The way in which caregivers display sensitivity in their nonsymbolic communication with infants may be related to the sensitivity needed in exchanges with children with severe disabilities. If service providers incorporate this degree of sensitivity in the classroom, communicative exchanges may be improved substantially.

Sensitivity in Caregiver-Infant Nonsymbolic Interactions

Literature on the caregiver-infant relationship describes the sensitivity of the caregiver as vital to the infant's communicative ability and progress (Bakeman & Adamson, 1984; Odom, 1983; Snow, 1984). Caregivers typically are sensitive to their infant's unique signals of readiness to communicate (e.g., the infant's direct gazing or leaning forward). the caregiver responds to these signals and allows the infant a turn during interactions and carefully waits until he or she is through responding (Clark & Seifer, 1983). Sensitivity to the child's behavior includes paying attention to his or her behaviors, focusing on his or her attention, reading the child's behavior as intent to interact, and responding contingently to the child's initiations (Dunst et al., 1987).

When caregivers are sensitive to the infant's cycles of attention and arousal, they allow their behavior to be temporally organized by the infant's actions. Caregivers learn to adjust their level of input to the child's varying responsiveness by being sensitive to his or her signs of readiness or nonreadiness for interaction. The infant's periods of attention to his or her caregivers provide a temporal frame for such professionals to organize the infants' behaviors and respond sensitively. The infants' face-to-face interactions are framed by a tendency for the caregiver to exhibit facial expressions when the children are attentive and to "turning them off" when they look away. The caregiver's ability to change or terminate interaction with the infant in response to such cues as gaze aversion, changes in body tension and facial expression, and lack of response from the infant are good indications of a caregiver's overall sensitivity to the infant's cues (Klein & Briggs, 1987). The caregiver's sensitivity to the infant's nonsymbolic modes of communication helps to encourage positive, satisfying interchanges.

In many respects, caregivers provide a kind of scaffold for the infant, responding to his or her communicative behaviors as if they were a part of a meaningful conversation (Bruner, 1977; MacDonald, 1985). Initially, caregivers may accommodate communicative deficiencies that infants have, by placing them in situations where the skills they lack are performed for them until the infant has learned to play the role of a communicative partner (Kaye, 1982). Caregivers tend to assess their communicative input and sensitively time it so that infants will receive the message when they are most able to understand. By being sensitive to the infant, caregivers can simplify their utterances to a point where the infant is just able to understand so that the caregiver's language input is one step ahead of the child's productive abilities (Bates et al., 1982). The sensitivity that caregivers exhibit facilitates comprehension of the infant's non-symbolic behaviors, demonstrating that nonsymbolic communication is a common and viable mode for relaying messages.

Strategies Used to Enhance Sensitivity

Recognize nonsymbolic behaviors
Respond contingently
Recognize individual's readiness for interaction
Respond to individual's level of communication

Sensitivity in Interactions with Learners who have Disabilities

Service providers of learners with severe handicaps can also successfully communicate with individuals who, similarly to the nondisabled infant, do not use language or symbols. Learners with severe disabilities who are functioning at a nonsymbolic level may communicate in a similar manner as the nondisabled infant. They may move unintentionally in ways that can be responded to as communicative, such as opening their mouth, turning their head, or blinking. It is important for service providers to observe these nonstandard behaviors and to recognize other subtle behaviors that could become attempts at communication. They need to recognize unusual cues and signals (e.g., open mouth, groans, yawn, change in muscle tone) as possible responses or attempts at "conversation."

Unfortunately, many caregivers and service providers demonstrate extremely low sensitivity to the communicative behaviors of the individual with severe handicaps, generally ignoring the individual's self-initiated behaviors (Houghton et al., 1987). Stillman and Battle (1986b) examined the forms of communicative behavior used by teachers of learners with severe multiple handicaps and found that directive forms were most frequently used. These forms often focused on a request for action or communication. The role that develops between the adult and learner is often characterized as a didactic relationship. This relationship usually lacks in turn-taking opportunities and confines the individual to a listener or responder role. It is speculated that the service provider is compensating for the inactivity of the individual, and attempting to maintain some degree of activity or interaction. The caregiver may also be attempting to elicit the level of behavior found in children without disabilities of the same age. By concentrating on the discrepancies that are seen between individuals with severe disabilities and those without disabilities inappropriate comparisons are established that are not conducive to providing a supportive environment for the individual with the disabilities. The desire to encourage the individual with disabilities to perform at a possibly unrealistic level may account for the frequency of directive behavior that is exhibited by caregivers.

Rowland and Stremel-Campbell (1987) describe the development of communicative competence in a sequence of levels, detailing the communicative behavior found at each level. The first level, involving preintentional behavior, represents reflexive or reactive behavior that occurs without the individuals' concious control. At the second level, the individual uses intentional behaviors (e.g., crying, fussing, reaching out), but not with the intent to communicate something specifically. The observers must infer the individual's intent. At the third level, the individual uses unconventional behavior with the intent of affecting the observer. Initiating eye contact, pushing away, whining or fussing may all be used to affect the observer's behavior. By the last level, the individual uses more conventional gestures such as pointing, giving, showing, or nodding to convey specific meanings. Service providers can increase their sensitivity to individuals with severe handicaps by recognizing these four different levels and accepting the *nonintentional* and unconventional behavior as communicative actions.

Caregivers and service providers who are able to read and anticipate the individual's cues and appear to "sense" the individual's receptivity and needs of the moment, may be responding to these early intentional and *nonintentional* forms of communication (Affleck et al., 1982; Newson, 1977). In addition, caregivers can learn to adjust their level of input to the individual's varying responsiveness by identifying his or her signs of readiness for interaction through these unconventional behaviors. Becoming familiar with the individual's nonsymbolic cues and responding sensitively to them may greatly enrich the individual's understanding of the world. An important aspect of this facilitative style is the adult's high level of responsiveness to learner-initiated interactions.

Example of Caregiver Sensitivity

Tim, a toddler with severe mental retardation, is fascinated by the bubbles his older brother is blowing. He excitedly vocalizes, gurgling and pointing at the bubbles as they float up into the air and then land on the ground and pop. His mother is nearby and responds to his gestures during his pauses, saying, "Yes, Tim, those are bubbles. Can you touch one?". Tim becomes excited again, reaching and pointing at the bubbles and looking at his mother in delight. His mother encourages him to continue expressing himself by responding appropriately to his nonverbal gestures and noises.

If caregivers and service providers can improve upon their observations of the individual's social and communicative behavior, they may develop increased sensitivity to the individual. The purpose in adjusting the interactional behaviors of caregivers should be to increase the likelihood of learners who will eventually understand the value of their behaviors. The caregivers will then be able to instill in these children a reason to communicate.

Responding to Nonsymbolic Communication

Maternal responsiveness is a very important component of sensitive caregiving behavior. Sensitive caregivers are responsive to their infants partially because of the fact that they have a considerable history of involvement with their infant that enables them to better interpret the baby's behaviors accurately. Before infants can communicate intentionally, caregivers attempt to interact with them by searching for behaviors in the infants' facial movements, vocalizations, and body gestures that could be interpreted as communicative responses. Bonds are strengthened by the caregiver's responsivity to the infant's nonsymbolic behaviors.

Caregivers play an essential role in interpreting and conventionalizing gestures of their infants. Their ability to discern the infants signals and assign meaning to their wide range of expressions promotes each communicative exchange. Some researchers have observed that infants whose mothers were most responsive in the first few months of life demonstrated increased communicative behavior toward the end of the first year, as compared to infants with less responsive mothers (Bell & Ainsworth, 1972; Odom, 1983). Sensitive caregivers exhibit a seemingly unconscious ability to perceive the infant's intent and respond appropriately. They transform what may appear to be random vocalizations and gestures into effective social signals. For example, the adult may monitor the infant's behavior, interpret him or her as having a certain intention, and then may attempt to partially or completely fulfill that intention.

These extremely responsive adult behaviors strengthen the relationship and promote the involvement of both members in the social exchange. Interactions dominated by the caregiver usually result in reduced responsiveness to infant behaviors. Caregivers who dominate interactions may miss natural opportunities to respond to their infants or may respond too quickly or too often. As a result, the infant has few occasions to initiate or control interactions. When caregivers are not concerned with eliciting specific responses, they can be more sensitive to the spontaneous behaviors of the infant that may be used to initiate an exchange.

Sensitivity in the Classroom with Individuals who have Severe Disabilities

Service providers of learners with severe handicaps can provide added benefits to their students by incorporating their natural characteristics (e.g., warmth, responsiveness) into their interactions in the classroom. Warm, socially responsive behavior is important for the infant. It facilitates both attachment and cognitive development. Just as the responsiveness of the caregiver can be related directly to the infant's success or failure in learning to communicate (Carlson & Bricker, 1982), the responsiveness of the service provider may directly influence the success of the learner with severe handicaps.

The individual with severe disabilities may exhibit subtle, unconventional behaviors that are often as unpredictable and difficult to interpret as intentional communication. It is especially important for the caregiver to develop high quality observational skills to assign meaning to these individuals' communicative expressions, and to be able to respond appropriately to them (Rowland & Stremel-Campbell, 1987). When service providers have become sensitive to the *unique* individual's signals, they may be better equipped to capitalize on opportunities that have been initiated subtly by the individual. By recognizing each individual's unique communicative cues, service providers can facilitate more enjoyable, meaningful exchanges with these individuals.

Example of Caregiver Responsiveness to Individual's Unique Communication

Jan, a paraprofessional, has been working with Sam, a 10-year-old boy who has cerebral palsy and a hearing impairment, at the school long enough to know that when Sam hangs his head back, he is bored with the present activity and wants to do something else. She is also aware that when he is interested in something, he remains quiet, but his eyes are intensely focused on the object of attention. She uses this knowledge to initiate new activities at an appropriate time. For example, when he hangs his head back and sighs, she initiates his favorite game (e.g., hide-and-seek), which helps to regain his attention (or eye focus) and involves him more with the other children.

The responsiveness of the service provider not only facilitates the interactive process, but, more importantly, fosters a feeling within learners that their actions can affect the environment (Lewis & Goldberg, 1969). The degree of responsivity found in the individual's social environment is instrumental in facilitating, for the individual, a sense of control over his or her surroundings. This in turn may promote the individual's cognitive and social development.

Building on Existing Communicative Skills

Another aspect of responding sensitively to nonsymbolic behaviors of both infants and individuals with severe disabilities includes building and expanding on the current communication skills of the learner. In the caregiver-infant dyad, caregivers structure the nonsymbolic communication setting in such a way as to build on whatever behaviors the infant spontaneously brings to the situation (Adamson & Bakeman, 1984; Newson, 1977). An excellent way in which caregivers can build on their infants' communicative behaviors is through imitation and expansion of the child's utterance. When the adult's vocal reinforcement contains an imitation of the child's sounds, it often prompts the child to vocalize again. In addition, caregivers who frequently expand on their child's vocalization or gestures have created perfect opportunities for increasing the interaction time. The child's communicative signal is received, interpreted, and elaborated in such a way that the child still recognizes his or her own initial sound or gesture, and is intrigued by the slight variation that the adult has added. This encourages the child to try to imitate the adult's expansion.

Folger and Chapman (1978) found that when adults expanded on the child's initial cue, the child responded frequently with an immediate imitation of the adult. Through this type of expansion or scaffolding, the caregiver is trying to elicit the most advanced behavior possible from the child. At the same time the caregiver wants to keep the social exchange fun, interesting, and at a level that the infant can easily comprehend. The mother's repetitions and expansions of the infant's utterances, based on the ongoing activity, situation, or infant's focus of attention, are an additional component of sensitive caregiver behavior that plays an important role in the acquisition of early communicative skills (Walker et al., 1982). The following is an example of how the caregiver builds on the individual's existing communicative skills:

Example of Building on the Individual's Existing Communicative Skills

Mrs. Hall, Mimi's babysitter, is absorbed in a television show and is not playing with Mimi. Mimi starts to fuss quietly, but when Mrs. Hall does not respond, she reaches out and grabs at Mrs. Hall's shoulder and vocalizes loudly. Mrs. Hall then responds, saying, "What do you want?" Mimi immediately grins and makes a funny face and sticks out her tongue. Mrs. Hall imitates her, taking turns as in their previous game, but this time Mimi is the one to initiate the faces and sounds. Mrs. Hall is responsive to Mimi's signals but is aware that it is important to build on these signals so that Mimi's communication repertoire expands. During their games, Mimi occasionally adds gestures and noises that Mrs. Hall has not seen before. Mimi kicks her legs up and claps her hands while she makes her funny sounds. Mrs. Hall responds to the new movements by imitating them and adding variations of her own.

Building on Existing Skills in the Classroom

The strategy of building on the child's existing skills, as seen in the caregiver-infant dyad, can be used readily in the classroom for students with severe handicaps. This instructional technique is a natural extension of a sensitive and responsive atmosphere in the classroom. The learner is seen as a central focus during instructional times. Rather than viewing the learner's disabling conditions as deficits that affect his or her overall interactive process, care is taken to focus on the learner's existing skills and to build from that level. The two strategies found in the caregiver-infant dyad—imitation and expansion of the child's communicative behavior—provide many opportunities for repeated positive interactions between the service provider and the learner with severe disabilities. A great advantage of this type of repeated interactions is that social exchanges can be elaborated on or complicated in order to stay at, or just beyond the individual's level of competence (Snow, 1984).

Rather than concentrating solely on the acquisition of new skills, the service provider can make maximum use of the individual's existing communicative skills in many educational settings. Building on learned communicative behaviors while targeting new skills may help incorporate more complex variations of the individual's existing repertoire. It is especially helpful to use the individual's newly learned skills repeatedly until they are performed without struggle or hesitation. Building on this act can then more easily involve other new variables.

Example of Expanding on Skills in the Classroom

Ian, an 8-year-old boy with severe disabilities, is learning how to signal the teacher that he would like more of an item or to continue an activity. During snack time, he signals that he wants more to drink by touching his hand to his mouth, looking at the juice pitcher, and sometimes vocalizing. The adults in the classroom have all learned to respond to this gesture and want to encourage him to use this behavior to initiate a request for his first drink at snack time. When it is time to pour the drinks, they purposefully wait close to him. Ian smiles and reaches for the pitcher. The teacher gets down to Ian's eye level and guides him to push the juice pitcher toward her and waits for eye contact. She does this to teach Ian to use his nonsymbolic behaviors in order to communicate with a social partner. She then helps him pour the juice.

Intervention programs should include both horizontal expansions (i.e., increasing the frequency of the use of a specific form of communication) and vertical expansions (i.e., enlarging on the complexity of an existing communicative behavior to encourage higher levels of communication). The purposes (i.e., functions) of the individual's communicative expressions can also be expanded so that the student learns to initiate requests for objects, actions, or attention, as well as to respond socially to protest, consent, or to greet people (Kaiser et al., 1987; Stremel-Campbell & Rowland, 1987).

INCREASING OPPORTUNITIES

Opportunities: Providing a favorable situation for participation, involvement, or advancement.

Role in communication: Increased awareness of communicative opportunities increases the likelihood of more social interactions. Creating additional opportunities promotes the individual's need and desire to communicate.

Role in caregiver-infant literature: Caregivers use the naturally occurring events of the day as opportunities to interact with their infants.

Role in nonsymbolic communication of individuals with severe disabilities: Service providers can allow more communicative opportunities to arise for individuals with severe disabilities in a variety of ways: allowing individuals to express their needs or desires (e.g., hunger, tiredness), by perceiving his or her communicative initiations, or by creating more opportunities (e.g., time-delay, choice).

Opportunity is described as a suitable occasion or a favorable set of circumstances for a chance to participate or to progress. For most of us, the opportunity for communication happens routinely throughout each day because communication is vital to our existence. Engaging in social activities, sharing intimacies with a companion, greeting others, or discussing important issues all require the intricacies of a commonly understood communicative system.

This section looks at the ways in which caregivers use naturally occurring events to spur communicative interactions between infants and themselves. It also considers how service providers may increase communicative opportunities in the classroom with individuals who have severe disabilities, by integrating the kinds of opportunities that occur daily in the caregiver-infant relationship. These daily occurrences generally result from the infant's need to communicate something to the caregiver (e.g., hunger, tiredness, discomfort). For the individual with severe disabilities, these natural needs also create opportunities for communication to arise. In addition, this section reviews ways in which the service provider can create or expand on communicative opportunities in the classroom.

Opportunities for Nonsymbolic Interaction

In order to learn to communicate, infants must have opportunities in which to interact with other people. Immediately after birth, newborn infants communicate to their parents by crying in discomfort when they need to eat, sleep, or have their diapers changed. During the first year, infants use a variety of nonsymbolic communicative behaviors to express their feelings, interests, and desires to their caregivers. During this presymbolic period, infants progress through the four levels of communicative competence described by Rowland and Stremel-Campbell (1987). Initially they cry, fuss, or move about expressing (and communicating) their state in a reflexive and unintentional manner. The caregiver attempts to understand these behaviors and responds dependably during this period, interpreting the meaning of the movements and vocalizations and attending to the infant's needs.

In the second level, the infant may intentionally move or exhibit gestures that communicate (e.g., regarding an object, averting eye gaze, moving away, or approaching someone), but the infant does not realize the effect that these behaviors have on the adult. When level III is reached, the infant is intentionally communicating by using the above behaviors, and then recognizes that these behaviors will produce particular responses in the caregiver. At the last level, the infant's nonsymbolic repertoire has developed to a more sophisticated level, where the gestures used are also conventionally used by other people (e.g., shrugging, pointing, extending objects, nodding). Caregivers respond reliably to all demonstrations in these four levels, thereby creating opportunities for further communicative exchanges.

The daily activities of feeding, diapering, and bathing create natural opportunities for communicative exchanges to arise between the caregiver and the infant. The time spent attending to the infant's physical needs becomes a natural opportunity to interact with the infant, providing a large percentage of the infant's daily communicative input. Caregivers cultivate the infant's communicative development by using many opportunities that arise during the day to elicit interactions.

Overlooking Communicative Opportunities

If caregivers did not respond to the infant's nonsymbolic communication, the infant would not survive. In fact, without communication attempts made, caregivers and infants would be virtually isolated from each other. People without communicative skills or any opportunities for communication are, in a sense, trapped within their own individual world of private sensations. The world of the individual with severe disabilities may not be far removed from this image of relative isolation. For many of these individuals, their limited communication abilities are their most serious handicap (Mount & Shea, 1982). Researchers are now reexamining the inclusion of these learners in institutions and school training programs where traditionally, learners have been expected to be passive and compliant. Recently, professionals are focusing on strategies that promote communicative opportunities in order to foster independence, self-reliance, and autonomy (Guess, Benson & Siegel-Causey, 1985; Halle, 1985; Peck, 1985; Shevin & Klein, 1984).

MacDonald (1985) observed that for many learners with severe handicaps, the need to communicate seems to have been eliminated from their environment. In most institutions and school settings, these individuals are dressed, fed, and cared for with minimal input expected or required of them. In fact, caregivers may be completely unaware of the amount of service they provide the individual without initiating communicative interaction. Unconsciously, routine tasks are taken care of quickly because it is so much easier and efficient. Well meaning service providers often inadvertently preclude a possible communicative interaction by performing daily tasks expediently (Halle, 1984). The individuals in this scenario learn to rely completely on their service providers (e.g., teachers, parents, therapists, paraprofessionals) and may exhibit a kind of learned helplessness (Seligman, 1975) because they perceive that they have no control over people or their environment.

Mittler and Berry (1977) speculate that individuals with severe disabilities are generally functioning at a level below their capabilities (especially in the area of communication), due, in part, to the failure of caregivers to provide appropriate opportunities for communication to occur in everyday settings. There is little reason for the individual to communicate a specific need or desire because their service providers unconsciously eliminate any natural requests by anticipating and providing for the individual's needs prematurely (Halle, 1985).

Similarly, adults may not expect students with severe disabilities to express themselves or to respond in any way during daily interactions. Adults may often talk in a rhetorical manner to an individual who has limited communicative abilities, answering questions for them and not seriously expecting them to respond. This rhetorical style probably develops over time because the service provider has not received consistent responses from the individual. Due to the individual's recurring lack of response to the adult's input, the adult might become accustomed to performing the individual's necessary daily activities without attempting to incorporate give-and-take communication (Halle, 1984).

Strategies Used to Increase Opportunities

Utilize time-delay
Provide choices
Create need for requests
Provide opportunities to interact

Perceiving Communicative Opportunities

There are several other factors that may contribute to service providers overlooking communicative opportunities with these children and thereby reducing their need to communicate. One important consideration is that many adults may not recognize the individual's own nonsymbolic communicative signals. In this highly verbal world, most people communicate primarily through speech. Speech is the most commonly used communication form, and yet it is the most complex since it involves the mastery of a learned, arbitrary symbol system. Individuals who function at a nonsymbolic level may not understand the complexity of a symbol system. Due to cognitive and/or neuromotor deficits, other individuals may never adequately develop speech that meets their communication needs. However, nonverbal, nonsymbolic communicative behavior is highly expressive and occurs in most infants long before verbal behavior (Bruner, 1975; Newson, 1977; Sachs, 1984; Yoder & Reichle, 1977). The nonsymbolic behavior of individuals who may not use symbolic communication can be equally expressive and functional.

Another trait exhibited by service providers and caregivers that might inadvertently affect the individual's need and desire to communicate is the tendency to expect a response from the individual only after a prompt, command, or question. Adults may only be aware of the individual as a communicator when they ask or prompt the individual to respond. Thus, the individual becomes indirectly dependent on the adult's prompts as the signal for communication and is compelled to be a responder, never an initiator (cf. Guess & Siegel-Causey, 1985). Unfortunately, the individual may have no need or desire to express anything at these specified moments. However, if the individual does not fulfill the adult's expectation, the adult may come to expect less and less communication from the individual. In time, the adult may not believe that the individual has any communicative needs.

Changing the views and expectations of parents, teachers, and other service providers toward the individual with severe disabilities may greatly improve their interactions (Affleck et al., 1982). Brown, Evans, Weed, and Owen (1986) found that various adult providers expressed a lack of confidence in the abilities of students with severe disabilities to problem-solve and request assistance. Perhaps due to this lack of confidence, service providers have developed the habit of doing everything for the individual with severe disabilities. During all types of daily activities, the individual's need or desire to communicate has gradually been extinguished.

Not only is there a limited need for the individual to communicate but also, service providers may demonstrate a tendency to disregard, ignore, or overlook possible child initiations. In the research done by Houghton et al. (1987), the majority of observed student interactions in the classrooms were ignored by attending staff members. One explanation for this may be that the nonstandard behaviors and vocalizations of the individual with severe handicaps are viewed as inappropriate or disruptive. Researchers have reported that caregivers of children who are experiencing severe language delays actually provide fewer opportunities for the individual to initiate communicative exchanges or to participate in turn-taking activities than caregivers of nonhandicapped children (Affleck et al., 1982; Walker & Kershman, 1981; Yoder & Kraat, 1983). These children, however, can be given the opportunity to see that their communicative attempts do have a purpose and that the environment can be affected by their displays.

Creating Communicative Opportunities

As already noted, when service providers anticipate the needs and desires of individuals with severe disabilities and fulfill them, they may be inadvertently inhibiting communicative attempts on the part of the individual. Individuals need to see the value in their communicative behavior in order to feel that they have a reason to communicate. To increase the motivation of individuals with severe disabilities, the behavior of the service provider can be changed to create more opportunities for these individuals to want to communicate.

It is interesting to note that researchers who are not involved with individuals with severe handicaps are focusing on the importance of recognizing and creating communicative opportunities for these individuals (Alpert, 1984; Mittler & Berry, 1977). Halle (1982, 1984, 1985) focused on arranging the environment to improve children's needs and motivation to communicate. One method that he described is the structuring of an interactive situation so that the individual must request something. For example, a learner may fully expect a teacher to provide a snack or toy at a certain moment; when the teacher hesitates (time-delay), the learner may become impatient and demand the teacher to follow through. The learner desires to have these expectations fulfilled and is motivated to vocalize or gesture in some way about them. The idea of the teacher delaying information, comments, or materials has been used commonly in the instruction of learners without disabilities. For example, a common practice seen in many school settings is for the teacher to hesitate after a question, prompting students to provide an answer. This allows students to relay what they know. Likewise, delaying assistance to a learner with severe handicaps prompts him or her to perform without help, and thus, display competency and understanding in that context.

Example of Creating Opportunities to Communicate

Howie, a student with moderate motor-impairment and hearing loss, is accustomed to the help his teacher provides when he needs to put on his coat for recess or at the end of the day. Occasionally, the teacher stands nearby but does not attempt to assist him. With much effort, Howie will get his coat off its hook and as he vocalizes, he reaches toward the teacher with the coat in his hands. The teacher responds quickly, "Howie, do you need help with your coat?" Howie vocalizes. "I will be happy to help you," his teacher responds.

Halle (1984) found that caregivers and teachers of individuals with severe language delay need to recognize and create new language learning opportunities. Musselwhite (1986) asks teachers and service providers, "Does the child have a need to communicate in this situation?" (p. 27). If individuals do not have a "need" to communicate, the objects, events, and actions of people need to be altered to create a reason for communicating. In essence, the environment should be arranged to evoke communication opportunties. Situations that appear to enhance social interactions (e.g., one-on-one interactions when the child is dressing, bathing, or going to bed) and high interaction context with others (e.g., mealtime, transportation times, activity periods) may be identified and analyzed to increase social participation for the individual with disabilities. When situations are provided that create a need for the individual to communicate, there is greater opportunity for an increase in self-initiated interactions and communicative behaviors.

Providing Choices and Decisions   Another strategy that can be used in natural settings at home or in the classroom involves providing individuals with opportunities for increased control over their environment (Peck, 1985). These opportunities include arranging aspects of the environment to provide the individual with situations that encourage self-initiated behavior and choice-making skills. Opportunities can be provided that prompt the individual to initiate an interaction or to make a decision involving the immediate situation. By integrating choice-making opportunities throughout the day, the individual is permitted to exercise initiative and to experience the consequences of personal decision-making (Shevin & Klein, 1984).

Through choice-making, learners are given the opportunity to learn from their mistakes or to experience success. This helps to develop a stronger self-concept and a more self-reliant attitude. Opportunities can be arranged that allow learners to perform for themselves, making them feel more effective and in control of their lives (Harrell & Strauss, 1986). Whether it is a choice between which game to play, which snack to eat, or what color toy to pick, the individual is encouraged to demonstrate control over the immediate situation, promoting decision-making and increased independence (Guess et al., 1985; Shevin & Klein, 1984). Within any given activity, the adult can arrange the setting to increase the number of choices or decisions that the individual has the opportunity to make. Within the routines of the day, individuals may have many occasions to choose among activities, desired objects, partners to play with, or whether or not to engage in an activity.

Example of Providing Choices

At snack time, the teacher comes by with a tray of juice and milk. She asks each student when she comes to him or her, "Do you want juice or milk?" as she points to the drinks. One child, Tammy, responds with a soft vocalization, turning her eye focus toward the juice glass. The teacher then guides her hand toward the glass and helps her place it on the table. Another child, Jack, does not respond, even when the question is repeated. The teacher says, "That's OK, Jack, if you don't want a drink. I'll check back with you later.

The above strategies can be incorporated as a part of incidental teaching strategies that may occur throughout the day (Hart & Risley, 1975). When the context is arranged to facilitate these opportunities, individuals have more reason to request help since they are strongly motivated to fulfill their specific desires (Halle, 1984). Education and rehabilitation settings need to offer the individual an array of options for increasing his or her quality and quantity of communication opportunities so that exchanges become more meaningful and relevant (Harrell & Strauss, 1986).

Service providers may overlook the needs of individuals to express choice because it is sometimes easier to choose for them. The individual's decision may create situations that were not expected. Sometimes in school and home settings, learner-initiated behaviors may be viewed as disruptive to the schedule or planned event. It is important for service providers to recognize the significance of decision-making, choosing, and initiating, and to determine the times and situations in which they can be flexible and allow the individual more of these opportunities.

Service providers can encourage other personnel to be accepting of the individual's choice, decision, or lack of response. It is important to emphasize that there are no right or wrong choices. If an individual chooses not to respond, the service provider can always return and ask the individual again, providing another opportunity. If there are no expectations for an individual's "appropriate" response, a more accepting atmosphere for decisions and choices will be created.

Like all people, individuals with severe disabilities need consistent opportunities throughout the day to express choice. When individuals with severe disabilities are overprotected, they are being denied their basic right to choose and to learn the consequences of their decisions. It is important that they are allowed to experience a sense of accomplishment, to try to make decisions or to perform independently, even at the risk of failure (Guess et al., 1985). Providing opportunities that enhance the individual's likelihood of becoming more independent and communicatively competent should be considered as much as possible throughout the day.

SEQUENCING EXPERIENCES

Sequence: Sequencing means to organize a related series of activities into a sequential, predictable format.

Role in communication: The use of ordered sequences increases the individual's familiarity with interactions and facilitates communication by promoting more active participation in social exchanges.

Role in caregiver-infant literature: Through the regularly recurring activities of the day, caregivers develop predictable patterns in their interactions with infants that help the children become more involved in their exchanges.

Role in nonsymbolic communication of individuals with severe disabilities: The arrangement of a definite sequence of activities helps to promote communicative interactions with individuals with severe disabilities by increasing their anticipation and involvement.

This section examines the literature on the topic of early interactions between caregivers and infants that focuses on the importance of establishing predictable routines throughout the day. It also considers how the integration of repetitive sequences within the classroom for individuals with severe disabilities may increase their participation and enhance social exchanges. In the caregiver-infant relationship, by organizing daily activities into a regulated, sequential format, the infants are allowed to become more familiar with the structure of the immediate environment. This familiarity encourages infants to participate more actively in interactions with their caregivers. Communication development is facilitated when infants recognize the patterns of a daily routine and can act as proficient members of a dyad, thus, assuming a definite role in the exchange. Investigators generally agree that during infant nonsymbolic exchanges, maternal utterances emitted in a specific order (i.e., as seen in games or repetitive sequences) help to establish a predictable, familiar environment for the child.

The opportunity to predict familiar events is vital to the infant's understanding of rules, structures, and other innate components of communication and language learning (Newson, Gregory, & Hartley, 1985). The infant is encouraged to develop gestural and vocal expressions that will function as effective social signals. As infants become increasingly aware of the social world, they learn to recognize their role in the context of familiar events and to anticipate the next occurrence (Rogow, 1984; Stillman & Battle, 1986c). The mutual use of a few shared understandings establishes a basis for further comprehension. This helps to continually expand the infant's cognitive consciousness and communicative awareness. The infant's signals, when emitted in a consistent context and interpreted by the caregiver in a consistent manner, promote later acquisition of communicative skills (Bruner, 1975; Rogow, 1984; Writer, 1987; Yoder & Reichle, 1977).

An important part of the infant's developing awareness of patterns and routines in communicative exchanges is the emerging sense of turn-taking. During these nonsymbolic exchanges, the infant acquires the turn-taking rules that underlie conversation (i.e., how to initiate, maintain, interrupt, and terminate vocal exchanges). Caregivers continually provide the infant with clues about conventionally appropriate gestures for signaling a turn in the conversation. When in synchrony, the caregiver and infant are observed to time their vocalizations to the vocal behavior of each other. Synchrony in timing is also observed between the infant's visual attention and the mother's facial expressions. When caregivers adjust to the on-off cycles of the infant's attention, they create a consistent, smooth sequence of exchanges that the infant can begin to recognize, respond to, and anticipate. This is similar to adult conversations, where turns are taken smoothly, alternating between speaking and listening (Kaye, 1982).

Strategies Used In Sequencing Experiences

Establish routines
Utilize patterns in games
Provide turn-taking opportunities
Encourage participation

Sequencing Experiences for Individuals with Severe Handicaps

For individuals with severe handicaps, the arrangement of a definite sequence of activities that includes repetitive practice can help to promote anticipation and involvement. There are a number of daily activities where successive routines are possible: self-help activities (e.g., dressing, bathing, preparing meals), leisure time activities (e.g., games, music), or at transition times (e.g., from school to home, from physical education class to lunch). A routine sequence of events can occur each day that is functionally related to the task at hand, giving the sequence added meaning. These regularized formats provide a useful structure that contain a kind of rule-bound framework. Over time, a consistent set of routines allows an individual with severe disabilities to become familiar with the routines of the day and to begin to feel more comfortable and secure within each activity.

The Individualized Curriculum Sequencing (ICS) model was first developed by Guess and colleagues (Guess et al., 1978) as an educational approach that incorporated the use of a sequence of skill clusters in the curriculum. This model is based on the theoretical assumption that learning is best achieved through the teaching of skill clusters that are meaningful and functional for the learner. Research on the effectiveness of the sequence model has been carried out for 5 years, proving its relevance for the population of individuals with severe handicaps (Helmstetter & Guess, 1987). (Readers may refer to the following citations for further information on the implementation of this curriculum model: Brown, Holvoet, Guess, & Mulligan, 1980; Holvoet, Guess, Mulligan, & Brown, 1980; Mulligan et al., 1980; and Sailor & Guess, 1983).

Arranging Sequences   Building recurring events in predictable sequences can provide many opportunities for communication if arranged properly within the setting of daily activities. For example, it is important to use the same signals or cues to announce the beginning or end of an activity (e.g., pulling chairs up to the table for snack time, an alarm ringing to end an activity). A repetitive sequence of exchanges can be embedded into each activity. This "redundancy" provides many opportunities for a child with severe disabilities to practice actions in a predictable format. With the building of recurring events, a child with severe multiple handicaps begins to anticipate what may happen next (Holvoet, Mulligan, Schussler, Lacy, & Guess, 1984; Writer, 1987). This establishment and maintenance of consistent daily experiences may increase the child's communicative role and promote further interaction skills.

Example of Repetition in a Daily Activity

During the school day, there are many activities that can incorporate the occurrence of a specific repetitive sequence. For example, any structured one-to-one activity can incorporate a sequence similar to the following:
Beginning:
1. Warning that activity will occur: Verbal cue combined with gestural cue—"John, lunch?" and guides John to make the gesture as if holding his lunch sack.
2. Participate in gathering materials: Adult gets near John but waits for him to get adult's attention. John leans forward to signal that he is ready to move forward. John is then helped to push his wheelchair to the refrigerator and he gets out his lunch sack.
3. Ready to do activity: The adult pauses and waits. John leans forward toward the doorway. The adult and John go to the cafeteria.
Ending:
4. Warning that activity is finished: After lunch, the adult uses a verbal cue combined with gestural cue—"All done?" and guides John's hands to feel empty food container.
5. Participate in putting away materials: Adult waits close to John until he gets their attention. John leans forward. The adult asks, "Oh, you are ready to go." John is guided to push his wheelchair and helped to put his lunch sack on a shelf.
6. Completion: The adult uses a verbal cue, saying, "Finished?" combined with gestural cue.
   This system of verbal and gestural cues at the beginning and ending of activities, coupled with specific communicative roles John must play, can be used at many different times during the day such as going outside, doing fine motor tasks, and having physical therapy.

Using Calendars   It is important that service providers keep the learner informed of the routine. One communication strategy uses the arrangement of objects or pictures to inform the learner of upcoming activities. This strategy has been identified by various names including anticipation shelves, concrete calendars, or calendar sytems (Stillman & Battle, 1984; Rowland & Schweigert, 1988; van Dijk, 1966, 1967).

Anticipation Shelf   An anticipation shelf is a row of objects. Each object is one that reminds the learner of a daily activity. The objects are arranged in the order of the learner's routine. They are separated from each other by partitions. At the end of the shelf is a box that is designated as the "finished box." The service provider and the learner go to the shelf before the first activity. The learner picks up the object (assisted as needed) and carries it to the activity. The learner uses the object within the natural unfolding of the activity. After the activity, they return to the shelf and put the object in the "finished box." Then they regard the object for the next activity.

Before initiating an anticipation shelf, the learner should be involved in a routine of activites. The activities should include some use of objects since almost every activity involves some type of object. For example, during lunch, the learner may use a spoon, plate, tray, cup, and napkin. Once the learner becomes familiar with the activity and the objects involved in it, the service provider may notice that right before lunchtime, the learner becomes excited (or upset) in anticipation of lunch upon seeing one of the objects. This behavior shows that an association has been formed between the object and the activity. At this point, the service provider can initiate an anticipation shelf by putting the object on a shelf near the activity and using it as described above. Once the learner shows that he or she anticipates lunch when getting the object off the shelf, another object for a different activity can be added. A partition is placed between the objects to convey that each object is related to a different activity.

The shelf should not be used to teach object/activity association because this is likely to take a long time and to result in the learner using the shelf in a mechanical way without any apparent understanding of the communicative value of the objects. Instead, the shelf should be used as a context and a method for conveying information to the learner.

Once the shelf is complete with one object for each activity, the service provider can begin to change the objects. The objects are changed to prevent the learner from making rigid associations between a particular object and a specific activity. Changing the objects teaches that what is important is not the relationship between the object and the activity, but rather that objects can be used to convey information. The objects are changed one at a time, and only when the learner consistently anticipates the activity upon getting the object. It is then changed to another object that the learner associates with the activity.

Calendar of Drawings   When the learner displays behaviors that indicate that an association has been formed between an object and an activity, then a calendar shelf can be initiated. A calendar of drawings is used in the same way as an anticipation or calendar shelf. There is one drawing for each activity the learner does during the day. The service provider and the learner go to the calendar. The service provider indicates the first drawing, the learner looks, and then they go to the activity together. When the activity is completed, they return to the calendar. When the service provider indicates that the activity is finished, they return to the calendar and look at the drawing for the next activity.

When the learner is responding easily to changes on the anticipation shelf, the service provider begins to work toward replacing the shelf with a calendar of drawings. The first step in introducing drawings is to teach the student that the drawing is like the object, and can be used in place of it. This prevents the learner from responding to the drawing as if it were simply another new object to carry to the activity. To begin, before each activity, the service provider and the learner obtain the appropriate object. They trace around the object and color the tracing. The service provider constantly draws attention to the resemblance between the drawing and the object. Then, they take the drawing and the object to the activity. When the activity is finished, they return the drawing and the object to the shelf. The next step in introducing drawings is by drawing each object as they look at it. The last step is to look at the object on the shelf and draw it from memory prior to each activity. Finally, the anticipation shelf can be replaced by a calendar of drawings of the objects that were on the shelf. At first, only one day is represented on the calendar, but as the learner becomes able to remember past events, and look forward to the future, a week can be represented. During the initial period of using a calendar, the learner may need to continue to carry the drawing to the activity to be able to remember the destination.

As with the anticipation shelf, the drawings on the calendar are changed as soon as the learner anticipates the activity upon seeing the drawing. The drawings are changed to prevent the learner from becoming too focused on the particular features of the drawing, and instead, focuses his or her attention on the use of drawings for communication. The first objective in changing the original drawings traced from the real objects is to help the learner to recognize drawings of objects that are not true to life size and color. The initial step is to change the drawings, one at a time, by eliminating the color. The next step is to change the line drawings, one at a time, to scaled down line drawings. Once the learner recognizes scaled down line drawings of the shelf objects, the drawings can be changed by adding details. For example, the calendar could include a drawing of the learner holding the shelf object, or the learner at the table with others and the object. Eventually it becomes unnecessary to include the shelf object in the drawing.

The calendar provides a good context for the service provider to engage the learner in conversation. During conversations, the service provider uses whatever forms of communication that are necessary to be understood, and offers the learner opportunities to communicate using whatever forms of communication the learner can produce. For example, the service provider indicates the grooming activity by pointing to the drawing and making a combing motion while holding the comb. The comb is then offered to the learner to invite the learner to use it to communicate. During the activity, the service provider observes the learner to see what he or she finds most interesting about the activity. The service provider communicates about the interesting details during the activity. Later, at the calendar, the service provider points to the drawing and communicates about the detail of the activity that caught the learner's attention. The conversation can be expanded by making a drawing of the interesting event and by communicating and giving the learner the opportunity to communicate as the drawing is made. Later in the day, they may look again at the drawing they made and continue to communicate about it.

Conversations around drawings are ideal for teaching the learner to recognize and use more communicative expressions. Some learners will be able to begin or to expand their use of symbolic communication while using the calendar. For the learner who has a large vocabulary and uses communcation productively, concepts such as color, number, weather, day, and date can be introduced through the calendar.

Increasing Social Awareness　Awareness of other people is a critical component in the development of communication. In communicative interactions, children learn the importance of social partners, the persons who receive their messages and provide contingent feedback. With the consistent structuring of daily events, children with severe disabilities may demonstrate increased participation and awareness of people. Through these exchanges, the child develops cognitively (e.g., through sequencing events) and socially (e.g., by recognizing other people as communicative agents).

In order to establish a particular communicative sequence, service providers should initially regard any signal from the child that is associated with the sequence as a communicative response, indicating the child's interest and involvement (Rogow, 1984). By participating in these interactions in a consistent framework, the child with severe disabilities learns to recognize other people as valuable social partners. Their shared activities lead to shared understandings. This then incorporates a salient part of communicative exchanges.

Example of Increased Social Awareness

At the start of establishing an integrated program, every afternoon the preschool classroom of children without handicaps meets for an hour with the children who have severe handicaps. The beginning of their group time together always starts with a familiar song that involves introducing each child to the rest of the group. To the tune of "Are You Sleeping," they sing, "Where is Emily, where is Emily . . .," taking turns substituting each child's name into the song. The service provider has a photograph of each child and as the song comes to its last line (for each child), the teacher gives the child their picture, while the song ends with, "There you are!" Emily is extremely happy to hear her name called over and over in the song. She is clapping her hands together and looking around the table at everyone. When the teacher extends Emily the photograph, she reaches for it excitedly and smiles broadly at the group. Everyday the children can anticipate beginning the session with the "Name Song." The more they hear the song, the more they participate in a fun activity that positively involves communication partners.

Patterns in Games   The recurrent patterns that exist within infant-caregiver games are a good example of the helpful framework provided by sequencing events. Social games in infancy possess several distinct features, including: (1) mutual involvement; (2) turn-taking; (3) a clear, repetitive structure; and (4) a small number of elements (Hodapp & Goldfield, 1983; Walker et al., 1982). Mutual involvement can be evidenced by simultaneous attention and interest in the ongoing activity of the dyad. It appears to be the prerequisite to social interactions, and a necessary condition out of which other actions may proceed (Hodapp & Goldfield, 1983). The second component—turn-taking—allows children to clearly comprehend their role in the interaction. This continuous exchange of turns establishes the timing and sequence of the game, and the need to pause in anticipation of the partner's turn. During the progression of a game, there are specific times for appropriate vocalizations that serve as markers during the interactions. In time, the reciprocal nature of turn-taking may evolve beyond the adult leading the interaction into a reversible-role game. Through repeated imitative exchanges, the child may assume the adult's original role and the adult can accommodate by taking on the child's role.

The third component—a clear repetitive structure—enables the infant to become immediately familiar and comfortable with the game context. Most games have an easily recognized sequence that occurs consistently throughout the game. The infant's use of repetition has been observed as a natural phenomena in nonsocial learning situations when they are exploring objects in their environment (Hodapp & Goldfield, 1983). The fact that repetition is an integral part of games capitalizes on the infant's natural tendency to learn through continual practice.

The last feature of games—a small number of elements and semantic relationships—aids in simplifying the structure and cycle of the game. The lack of complexity and extensive vocalizations allows the infant to easily comprehend the rules and sequence of the game without a sophisticated foundation in language.

Example of Reciprocity seen in Games

Mimi, a 14-months-old, watches her babysitter, Mrs. Hall, making funny faces. Mrs. Hall says, "Watch me make a funny face," crinkles her nose, sticks out her tongue and rolls her eyes. Mimi watches closely and then tries to crinkle her nose. She opens her mouth, and sticks out her tongue and laughs. Then Mrs. Hall says, "I'm going to make funny noises." She gurgles and makes nonsense sounds. Mimi then mimics Mrs. Hall, vocalizing an "aahh" and adding another funny face. They alternate, back and forth, taking turns making faces and funny sounds.

Use of Games for the Individual with Severe Disabilities

Since games typically follow simple rules and exemplify the structure of a conversation, they can provide a reliable setting for individuals with severe handicaps to learn that their behaviors do have predictable outcomes. Repeated performances enable these learners to discover that their actions can bring consistent results from the service provider. The service provider can imitate or elaborate on the individual's behavior, thus holding the individual's attention as they are both focused on the same subject. In games, anticipation is shared within a predictable sequence of events.

The pauses that occur naturally in games between infants and caregivers can help to establish the concept of turn-taking when used in exchanges between service providers and individuals with severe disabilities. These pauses cue individuals to take their turn and to allow them to participate more actively and expect the next turn. The individual with severe disabilities may then gradually develop an increased understanding of their roles in the exchange and may assume more responsibility, eventually initiating game sequences. Service providers can also respond to the reflexive or unintentional behaviors of the individual with severe disabilities as if they were intentional. Through repeated experiences in a game, early behaviors of the individual with severe disabilities, that were at first unintentional, may become intended responses to keep the game sequence going or to achieve a particular goal. This is due in large part to the service provider's sensitive responding to the learner's first behaviors as if they were intentional.

The give-and-take structure of game playing provides a useful format in which to regulate the behaviors of the individual with severe disabilities. Responding sensitively and appropriately to the individual's behaviors within a game sequence can increase participation and awareness within interactions with other individuals. The consistent patterns of games help to establish a firm foundation for more complex communicative exchanges.

Example of Increased Participation through Games

Holly, a child with severe multiple disabilities, loves to play the game "pat-a-cake" because her friend, Lisa, from the first grade has taught her the hand movements and she likes it when they clap their hands together. Holly feels that Lisa is her "pat-a-cake" partner and she often seeks her out at recess so that they can play the game together.

When she finds Lisa on the playground, she will smile and bring her hands together, which signals to Lisa that she wants to play their special game. Before Lisa taught Holly the game, Holly had no real interest in interacting with the other students.

Contingency in Social Routines   In the nonsymbolic exchanges that emerge between both infants and their caregivers and children with severe disabilities and their caregivers, the establishment of contingency in social routines plays an important role. In the caregiver-infant dyad, infants are constantly searching their environment for signs of a synchronous relationship between their own actions and related outcomes. It is pleasurable to the young infants to recognize that their behavior can cause events to happen. For young infants the awareness of the ability to control events within their surroundings is crucial. When they are able to detect a contingent relationship between their behavior and environmental outcomes, they are further motivated to respond and attend to their surroundings. Occasions that promote contingency awareness are important for the infants' development and help them to be more effective learners in later contingency tasks (Schweigert, 1987).

Social routines and games provide a setting for the infant and caregiver to have many "contingent" experiences. The structure of routines provides consistent opportunities for the infant's behaviors to be responded to immediately, appropriately, and reliably. The adult's responses are contingent upon the infant's behaviors in that they are conditioned by and dependent on the infant's cues. In addition, the clear, repetitive structure of routines enables the infant to become immediately familiar with the context and with the reliable responses of the adult. A partnership is formed during routines since each participant relies and requests meaningful feedback. The more apparent and predictable the child's signals, the more the adult can respond contingently.

It is important to remember that the caregiver and the young child with disabilities are continually influencing each other during their early communicative exchanges. Contingent interactions may be difficult for the caregiver to establish with the young child with disabilities as a result of his or her less predictable responses, as well as the influence of disabling conditions on the interactional process. For example, many high-risk infants demonstrate behaviors that are inconsistent and hard to understand. These infants may be difficult to arouse or soothe. They may make very little eye contact or frequently exhibit gaze aversion, presenting a significant challenge to most parents. When the infant's responses and behaviors are difficult to read, the caregiver has a much harder time understanding the infants communicative attempts and responding appropriately. The readability, predictablility, and responsiveness of the infant affects that of the mother (Stremel-Campbell & Rowland, 1987). The resulting lack of contingent responses from the caregiver creates a confusing and possibly stressful environment for the infant.

A similar situation is observed in the development of interactions between adults and individuals with severe disabilities. What the individual learns about the communication process and about him- or herself as a communicator is greatly influenced by the social role that evolves in his or her surrounding environments. Individuals with severe disabilities are often relegated to a passive, noninteractive role in their environment due to reduced sensory capabilities and a limited response repertoire. The reduced experience of contingent interactions may have significant consequences not only for the individual's communicative development but also for learning, motivation, affective, and cognitive development.

Consequently, it is crucial that an intervention program be provided that ensures opportunities for the individual to facilitate active participation in the world. For the individual with severe handicaps, the service provider may need to respond broadly at first to most forms of the individual's behaviors. As the adult becomes more familiar with the individual's communicative behaviors, the responses can become more individualized, relevant, and contingent. Since individuals with severe disabilities function at different levels of intentionality (Rowland & Stremel-Campbell, 1987), caregivers must be careful to provide contingent responses regardless of the levels of intentional or nonintentional behavior performed by the individual. By receiving contingent, positive reinforcers from the caregiver, individuals with severe handicaps begin to recognize that their attempts at communication can be successful. They find that they do have the capacity to influence people and their environment and that they are responded to in turn.

Routines and games clearly shape an understanding of reciprocal roles by providing a setting for mutual exchange (Rogow, 1984). Through repeated experiences during games, gestures that are made in response to the adult become intentional. Gradually, these gestures are performed to achieve a specific goal. Infants and children with severe handicaps may gradually become aware of their ability to change or manipulate the responses of the caregiver. When the daily ritual of games and routines is well established, the individual with severe disabilities is able to demonstrate more control over a course of events.

Example of Contingency in Social Routines

The first time Joey saw his older sister play peek-a-boo, he just giggled when she hid herself under a blanket and came out unexpectedly. However, after a few repetitions, Joey appeared to want to hide under the blanket and suprise his sister, too. He reached for the blanket, fussing and grunting in his determination to be the one hidden under the blanket. His sister cooperated by throwing the blanket over him and then feigning suprise, she called out, "Peek-a-boo," as he popped out at her.

Once the individual is comfortable with a routine, some deviation from the structure may be effective in encouraging further anticipation and interest. Any individual with severe disabilities can benefit from the structuring and restructuring of specific games or routines. A slight change within a clear, repetitive routine will further enhance anticipation and involvement. In fact, altering a well-established routine slightly is an ideal way to create a "need" for the child to communicate. As previously discussed, the disruption of an anticipated action can prompt the child to communicate by questioning or requesting information. It is important that classroom routines do not become so consistent that learners are over-programmed and dependent on the exact routine to function effectively. For the individual with severe disabilities, early contingency awareness in the social sphere and the development of a reliable means of social responding are key components in building social communicative skills.

UTILIZING MOVEMENT[1]

Movement: Refers to methods of adult and child participation in reciprocal exchanges and interactions that involve movement.

Role in communication: The use of movement encourages communication by developing the individual's: 1) awareness of self; 2) separation of self from the environment;, 3) recognition of others as responsive, social partners; and 4) understanding that movements can convey messages.

Role in caregiver-infant literature: Infants first explore their world through the movements that form a primary foundation for early learning.

Role in nonsymbolic communication of individuals with severe disabilities: Children with severe disabilities may be focused on themselves and may need encouragement to explore their environment. Movement activities help to stimulate their awareness of the world and may contribute to their responsiveness to social partners.

Utilizing movement as strategy for enhancing communicative skills has its foundation in studies of presymbolic social-communicative interactions. Research on early caregiver-infant interactions offers a rich description of how caregivers engage in movement "dialogues" with infants who have not yet acquired language (Bates, 1976; Bruner, 1977; Newson, 1979; Schaffer, 1977). Caregivers utilize movements to communicate, to attach communicative meaning and purpose to movements that the infant makes, and to establish the pattern through movements of reciprocity and joint focus that underlies both symbolic and nonsymbolic communicative exchanges. Werner and Kaplan (1963), in their theory of the development of symbolic abilities, also viewed movement as playing a fundamental role in the acquisition of communicative abilities. They suggested that through observing, participating in, and imitating the movements of others, the infant develops a nonsymbolic vocabulary for understanding movements as communications and for using movements to communciate.

Strategies Used to Utilize Movement

Respond to movements as communicative behaviors
Use movements matched to the level of the learner's actions
Select movements that accommodate the learner's immediate ability
to respond and interact within particular contexts/moments
Use movements as communicative behaviors

For normally developing infants, a movement-based receptive and expressive vocabulary is a temporary stage leading to the acquisition of language. Within this stage, however, there are many important steps. These steps were extracted by van Dijk (1965a, 1966, 1967, 1986) from Werner and Kaplan (1963) and reformulated into an intervention approach for use with learners with dual sensory impairments or who have severe, multiple disabilities. The focus of this approach was on movement as the form of communicating, reciprocity as the pattern, and "distance" as the substance and measure of communicative development.

Distance has many facets. It refers, in part, to the learner's increasing attentiveness and

---

[1]Robert Stillman and Christy Battle contributed to this section.

responsiveness to communications by having decreased perceptual saliency; to the learner's increasing ability to understand and use communciations outside the particular content in which they were learned; and to the learner's increasing ability to understand and use abstract forms of communication (e.g., body movements, representational objects, depictive [iconic] gestures, symbols).

Anyone who observes normally developing infants is aware of the amount of time they devote to interacting with others and learning about their world. Many learners with severe, multiple disabilities, however, because of sensory, physical, and mental impairments, may be restricted in their ability to interact. For some, it seems as though their interest in the world extends no further then their own bodies. Their engagement with the world seems limited to obtaining stimulation and satisfaction of basic physical needs. Observation of these differences was noted by van Dijk (1965a, b), particularly between the outwardly directed focus of the nondisabled infant and the more isolated inwardly directed focus of the learner with severe, multiple disabilities. He proposed that learners with severe, multiple diabilities need the encouragement and assistance of others to help them develop an interest in the world outside themselves (van Dijk, 1965a, b, 1986).

The method that van Dijk developed invites the learner's interest in the world through encouraging his or her participation in nonsymbolic communicative interactions. By focusing on movement as the primary means of interacting, van Dijk's method emphasizes the idea that actions are the learner's first vocabulary for interacting with the physical and social world. He advises that if adults wish to establish contact with inwardly directed learners, they must begin at the learner's level by adopting an action vocabulary that engages the learner in interactions. The adult responds to the learner's action vocabulary and *uses* the learner's action vocabulary when interacting with the individual. Van Dijk suggests that one must enter the learner's world by being cognizant of the learner's unique repertoire of actions and action-based understanding of the world.

Opportunities for communicating and learning through movements are present throughout the day. Therefore, van Dijk's approach is best viewed as an organizing framework used to incorporate communication into all of the learner's daily activities. Movements are also, generally, a familiar and enjoyable experience for learners and provide a valuable point-of-entry for engaging and maintaining them in communicative interactions.

Responding to and Using Movements as Communicative Behaviors

The service provider might best begin to engage the learner in an interaction by observing the actions that are made or those of interest and then utilizing these actions as a focus for communicating.

Example of Utilizing Movement

Toby is seated on the floor with a large ball on top of his outstretched legs. He is lightly tapping his head on the ball and it rolls away from him and back again as he repeats the tapping movement. The paraprofessional joins Toby on the floor and puts her legs around his as she faces him. The next time Toby taps the ball with his head, the paraprofessional puts her head down and taps it back to him. They begin a reciprocal game of passing the ball back and forth across their legs. As Toby adds actions of rocking backwards and then tapping the ball, the paraprofessional adds these same actions. Occasionally, she pauses when the ball reaches her. Toby then reaches for her head and she responds to Toby by tapping the ball with her head. Thus, the adult can use movements as communicative behaviors that match the learner's level of understanding.

A description of the whole van Dijk's approach is beyond the scope of this book. His ideas, however, are infused throughout the content. For a description of aspects of the van Dijk approach the reader should refer to the following acticles in the References section: Stillman and Battle (1984), van Dijk (1965a, b, 1967, 1986), and Writer (1987).

Selecting Movements to Enhance Communication Interactions

In utilizing movement as a strategy for communication, it is important for the service provider to look beyond the physical form of the movement and to focus on what the learner is likely to receive, anticipate, and understand. From this focus on the learner as the recipient of the communication, the service provider can determine:

1. How salient the movement must be for the learner to detect and understand it as a communication.
2. How important the physical and temporal context is in supporting the learner's understanding of the movement as a communication.
3. How closely the movement must resemble what the service provider intends to convey in order for the learner to understand the messege.

Each of these considerations refers to an aspect of distance and so each incorporates a continuum. It is this continuum to which service providers should refer in their efforts to select communications that both convey information and enhance their learner's communicative abilities. In addition, service providers should consider how communicative movements can be incorporated within daily activities and in a manner that encourages reciprocal interactions. In this way, service providers will not be tempted to concentrate on communication only in isolated "communication activities" or focus only on training the learner to perform particular communicative behaviors.

Salience of the Movement   The salience of the movement refers to how easy the movement is for the learner to detect. Communicative movements that are most salient and, therefore, most easy to detect, are those that incorporate physical contact between the service providers and learner. Communicating through movements while in physical contact is most important when interacting with learners who do not consistently attend or respond to communications at a greater distance (i.e., without tactile/kinesthetic cues). Movement with physical contact helps draw the learner's attention to the service provider's actions and set the stage for the learner to develop an understanding that movements may be used to affect each other's behavior.

Movements in physical contact, although an effective means of communicating, have several drawbacks. The repeated physical stimulation from physical contact may cause the learner to focus more on the pleasurable sensations associated with the movement than on the service provider's purpose for communicating. The learner might become a passive recipient rather than an active participant in the interaction. Furthermore, reliance on physical contact limits the learner's opportunities for communicating to those times when physical contact between him or her and the service provider are possible. Thus, communicative movements in physical contact should be viewed as a temporary approach that is useful in: 1) establishing initial communications (e.g., interactions or communicative behaviors of the learner), 2) patterns of reciprocity in interactions, and 3) occasions for clarifying communications and activities that are being introduced to the learner.

Movements can also be made more salient by exaggerating them and selecting ones that use or affect the whole body. Movements made by the whole body even without physical contact are easier to detect than smaller movements made by the head or limbs. Head and limb movements, in turn, are easier to detect than hand or finger movements. As the learner recognizes movements as communications and consistently attends to the service provider's actions, the saliency of the movement becomes less important.

Physical and Temporal Context   The learner's understanding of a particular communicative expression may rely not only on the saliency, but the context in which the communication occurs. At first, the learner may only understand a communicative behavior given at a particular time in a particular place. For example, the learner is able to respond to the service provider's throwing motion over the wastebasket to request that he or she throw the paper towel away after drying his or her hands in the bathroom after lunch. When the service provider makes the throwing motion toward the wastebasket from a position by the sink before the learner finishes drying his or her hands, however, the learner might not respond. It is likely, in the first situation, that physical context (e.g., proximity of the wastebasket to the learner and the service provider) aided the learner to understand the service provider's gesture. In addition, aspects of the temporal context (i.e., the learner's knowledge that throwing the towel away comes after drying hands) also helped the learner to understand the service provider's communication. When the physical and temporal features are changed, the learner can no longer recognize the meaning of the service provider's action. Thus, it is critical that the service provider consider the importance of the context in enabling the learner to understand and respond to communications.

The least advanced learners might respond best when the communicative movement is used in the same physical and temporal context as the action to which it refers.

Example of How Physical and Temporal Context Effects Actions

The service provider can use a scooping action to request Sid to eat when he is at the table with the bowl in front of him, holding his spoon. The service provider communicates with the scooping action in the same physical and temporal context in which it is being displayed.

Gradually, the service provider can begin to introduce distance between the communication movement and the action to which it refers. For example, temporal distance is introduced when the service provider uses the motion before the student has the spoon in hand. Even more temporal distance is established when the scooping motion is used before the learner has his or her plate. Physical and temporal distance are introduced when the service provider uses the scooping motion outside of the context of the table. For example, the motion is used to indicate lunch at the close of the previous activity. Each time the service provider tries to incorporate more distance between the communication movement and the action, he or she must assess the learner's response to make sure that the learner still recognizes the communication even though elements of the context have changed. Whenever a learner fails to respond, the service provider should move the communication movement closer to the action to which it refers in time and space to facilitate the learner's understanding. Whenever the learner consistently responds to an expression, the service provider should attempt to provide an increment of distance between the movement and the indicated action to expand the student's ability to respond to the expression.

Resemblance of the Movement to the Message   Another feature to consider when selecting communicative movements to use with a particular learner is the resemblance of the movement to the message. Some forms of communication closely resemble the object or action to which they refer. For example, a pantomime of drinking looks like the drinking action, a drawing of a person standing looks like the person standing, and when one meows like a cat, it sounds like the cat. Some forms of communication bear no resemblance to the action or object. For example, the word "dog" does not look like or sound like a dog, tapping the learner's head to indicate combing does not look like the combing action, and patting the chair to indicate sit does not look like the sitting action. The closer the resemblance between the communication and the message, the easier it might be for the learner to understand it. Therefore, at first, the learner would be most likely to understand the message if the movement and the message are identical. For example, the service provider could indicate "combing" by moving the learner's hand with the comb through the learner's hair. Once the learner responds consistently to an expression that is identical to the indicated action, however, it is important to introduce some distance or some lack of similarity between the expression and the message. For example, when the learner responds to the combing gesture of the previous example the service provider can try making the combing movement in her own hair to indicate combing to see if the learner can understand a more sophisticated expression. As the learner shows an understanding of the expression by responding to it consistently, the service provider can change to an expression that shares fewer features with the action. For example, the service provider could make the combing movement in his or her own hair without the comb in hand. Whenever the learner fails to respond to an expression, it may be because there is not enough similarity to the action. At that point, the service provider should use an expression with closer resemblance to the action. Whenever the learner responds to an expression consistently, the service provider should try changing the expression slightly so that it does not resemble the action so closely. This helps to expand the learner's ability to respond to increasingly abstract forms of communication.

Incorporating Communication Movements into Daily Activities

Communicative movements can be used to convey information to the learner anytime the service provider wishes to get a message across, regardless of the activity or the setting. If the service provider wants to request that an older learner clear the table, take his or her turn in bowling, button his or her shirt after swimming, pick up his or her tray at the fast food restaurant, put the quarter in the machine at the laundromat, or sweep up the hall in the school, movements can be used to convey these requests in a manner that the learner can understand and respond to appropriately. If the service provider wants to ask the younger child to throw the ball during gym, clap his or her hands during music, or pick up the paint brush during art, movement can be used to convey these messages. Movement can also be used to instruct the learner in actions. For example, the service provider can use movement to show the learner how to spread peanut butter on a sandwich, open a jar of pickles, tie his or her shoes, dig a hole in the sand box, or put labels on jars in the work place.

Movements can be used to give information to the learner by describing the action or object. For example, the service provider can describe the learner's drawing action by making a drawing action or by touching the learner as he draws. Sorting silverware can be described by mimicking the learner's actions as sorting occurs or after sorting is done. In order to use movements as effective communicative behaviors, the service provider must be attuned to whether the learner is responding to the communications. If the learner is consistently responding, then the service provider can make the movements more complex. If the learner is not responding, then the service provider can make the movements simpler with regard to the dimensions of saliency, context support, and resemblance of movement to the message.

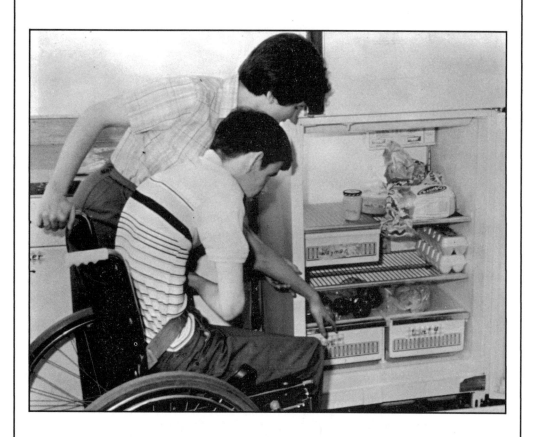

PROCEDURES FOR ENHANCING NONSYMBOLIC COMMUNICATION

Ellin Siegel-Causey, Christy Battle,
and Barbara Ernst

The purpose of this section is to demonstrate the ways in which the five instructional guidelines (e.g., developing nurturance, enhancing sensitivity, sequencing experiences, increasing opportunities, and utilizing movement) can be implemented by service providers. The strategies are linked to specific purposes:

Providing Nurturance: To foster an atmosphere of warmth and security, by providing sustenance and support.

Purpose: Builds an individual's sense of trust in the service provider and secure feeling within the environment.

Strategies: Provide comfort, support, and affection.
Create a positive setting for interactions.
Expand on child-initiated behavior.
Focus on individual's interest.

Enhancing Sensitivity: To perceive, interpret, and respond to nonsymbolic behaviors in a sensitive fashion that is appropriate and satisfying to the recipient.

Purpose: Facilitates communicative behavior and awareness of another person as an important agent in social interactions.

Strategies: Recognize nonsymbolic behaviors.
Respond contingently.
Recognize individual's readiness for interaction.
Respond to individual's level of communication.

Increasing Opportunities: To create and facilitate situations that allow the learner to communicate in natural exchanges.

Purpose: Aids communication by promoting opportunities for individuals to participate in communicative exchanges.

Strategies: Utilize time-delay.
Provide choices.
Create need for requests.
Provide opportunities to interact.

Sequencing Experiences: To establish routines in order to organize experiences for the learner.

Purpose: Increases the individuals' familiarity with routine interactions, allowing them to take a more active role in the give-and-take of social exchanges.

Strategies: Establish routines.
Utilize patterns in games.
Provide turn-taking opportunities.
Encourage participation.

Utilizing Movement: To utilize the partnership of adult and child by participating in reciprocal exchanges by using movements to convey information to learners and by promoting the learner's use of movements to communicate with others.

Purpose: Promote communication by: 1) enabling the learner to understand the expressions of others, 2) giving the learner an effective method for communicating, and 3) helping the learner to recognize others as responsive social partners.

Strategies: Respond to movements as communicative behaviors.
Use movements matched to the level of the learner's actions.
Select movements that accommodate the learner's immediate ability to respond and interact within particular contexts/moments.
Use movements as communicative behaviors.

The manner in which each of the above guidelines is incorporated into a daily context depends upon the individual's current communicative functioning and the specific communication goals for that individual. The previous sections have presented the philosophical orientation and literature support for the instructional guidelines. It is important that the philosophy of the instructional guidelines be understood in order to avoid a "step-by-step cookbook" approach to communication intervention. Therefore, this section uses examples of interactions in a dialogue-like format. The reader is encouraged to "act out" the dialogues. In addition, space is provided to allow the reader an opportunity to utilize the intervention techniques by creating purposes for an individual learner's communication intervention using the five instructional guidelines (refer to pp. 23–52, this volume). The dialogues were written with a focus on "moments" of interactions that emphasize communicative intervention. It is assumed that implementation of appropriate instructional strategies and best-practices methods will be part of every service provider's programming, including intervention in nonsymbolic communication. These methods, however, were not detailed within the dialogues so that the philosophy of this intervention book and the intervention guidelines could be emphasized.

Descriptions of interactions between service providers and learners who are severely disabled and who use nonsymbolic communication are presented in the following pages. These interactions are displayed in a dialogue-like format depicting learners of various age levels (e.g., 3–15 years of age) and many handicapping conditions including motor impairments; hearing loss; blindness; moderate, severe, and profound retardation levels; and aggressive behavior. The interactions occur in a variety of contexts including mealtimes, self-care activities (e.g., diapering, doing laundry, grooming), leisure activities, physical education, community-based instruction (e.g., eating in a restaurant), and social interactions within school and community settings. In this section, five learners are depicted in a series of three dialogues apiece. Each learner is introduced with a description of communicative level and impairments. A description of the purposes for each learner's communication intervention is also included in this introduction to the dialogues.

The interactions depict the use of the instructional guidelines that are outlined in Section 2. Within each dialogue, in the left hand column, the adult behaviors have been labeled, identifying the specific intervention guideline and strategy used. Each strategy has been defined according to the subheadings listed in Table 3. These subheadings provide an additional description of the adult intervention behavior. The adult's use of an intervention guideline is noted within the dialogue by **bold** lettering in the adult column. In many cases, the adult's behaviors could incorporate more than one guideline or more than one subheading under each guideline. Due to limitations in space, however, only one guideline has been identified to clarify each adult behavior. The process of relating specific adult behaviors during mock interactions with students should facilitate the reader's understanding of the interrelated nature of the intervention guidelines.

Begin reviewing the dialogues by reading the description of the learner and the summary of the communication intervention. After reviewing the learner's description, it is suggested that as the dialogues are read that a picture of the flow of the interaction that takes place be noted. Throughout the following dialogues, ***bold italics*** in the learner script designates the learner's use of nonsymbolic behavior. After the dialogue has been completely read, it may be of benefit to then review the interaction again by reading the adult and learner actions, noting the bold type, and looking to the left column that lists the corresponding guideline that is being used.

Table 3. Intervention guidelines and strategies illustrated in dialogues

Guidelines	Strategies
Developing Nurturance	Provide support, comfort, affection Create positive setting for interactions Expand on child-initiated behavior Focus on individual's interest
Enhancing Sensitivity	Recognize nonsymbolic behaviors Respond contingently Recognize individual's readiness for interaction Respond to individual's level of communication
Increasing Opportunities	Utilize time-delay Provide choices Create need for requests Provide opportunities to interact
Sequencing Experiences	Establish routines Utilize patterns in games Provide turn-taking opportunities Encourage participation
Utilizing Movement	Respond to movements as communicative behaviors Use movements matched to the level of the learner's actions Select movements that accommodate the learner's immediate ability to respond and interact within particular contexts/moments Use movements as communicative behaviors

Description of Amy and
Purposes for Her Communication Intervention

Amy is 3 years old. Her muscle tone is very stiff making it difficult for her to move. She can reach and grasp, and attempts to eat and wash independently. She needs help to move around and uses adaptive equipment to sit up.

Amy has a mild hearing loss, but she is still able to enjoy music and singing. She always looks when her teachers call to her. Her teachers are always careful to make an effort to speak so that Amy can hear. They also try to eliminate any extraneous background noise when they are working with her.

Amy does not understand any language. Her teachers know that this is not caused by her hearing loss but by the fact that, despite her years, she still does not understand language. Therefore, when her teachers want to communicate something to her, they have to do it in a way that Amy will understand. They use all kinds of nonsymbolic cues to communicate with Amy. For example, to communicate that it is time for lunch, they have lunch at the same time, after the same activity, in the same place, with the same adult, using the same bib, spoon, bowl, and placemat every day. Every day they follow the same procedure to get to the lunch area. Eventually, Amy comes to understand that when gym is finished, and the lunches arrive in the room, then Carol will come to get her. Amy can learn to anticipate Carol showing her the bib and pointing to the lunch table. Carol then takes Amy to the table, saying, "Lunch." Amy sees her placemat. Carol shows Amy the spoon, she sits her at the lunch table, presents her with her bowl, and then Amy knows it is time to eat lunch.

Amy also communicates using nonsymbolic communication. She communicates primarily by taking and moving the adult's hand. For example, if Amy wants a bite of food, she pulls the adult's hand with the filled spoon in it to her mouth.

Amy's dialogues occur during diaper changing (#1), at lunch (#2), and in a visit to a community preschool (#3).

PURPOSES FOR AMY'S COMMUNICATION INTERVENTION

Developing Nurturance

Develop a warm, affectionate relationship with the new teacher, Carol.

Create an atmosphere that provides plenty of support and affection that will encourage Amy to become more aware of people and communicative opportunities.

Focus on Amy's particular interests of the moment, expanding on behaviors in which she initiated.

Develop a positive environment that helps Amy enjoy interaction with others and encourages her involvement in more communication exchanges.

The people who are involved with Amy's education are using several strategies to encourage her to communicate. They realize that Amy's desire and ability to communicate rests, in large part, on the development of positive relationships between her and those with whom she interacts. In order to encourage the development of positive relationships, her service providers are supportive and affectionate toward Amy. They try to make her activities playful, fun, and interesting so that she will associate her service providers with pleasurable experiences.

In the following dialogues, Carol, the teacher, tries to convey her affection and support of Amy by using an encouraging and affectionate tone. For example, she responds enthusiastically to many of Amy's behaviors: "Amy's looking!", "Yes, go change!", "Yes, down!", "That's right! Amy is wet", "Amy pulls!". She often says, "You're doing great!" as she pats Amy on the back, and, "You're my girl!" as she kisses and pats Amy.

Both Carol and Jeanne, a speech-language clinician, try to make their activities interesting to Amy. Carol does this by focusing the interaction on what Amy is currently doing. For example, during diapering, when Amy looks at the shelf of diapering materials, Carol detours in the activity to focus on the objects on the shelf. Later, when she notices that Amy is looking at her, she responds to Amy's focus of attention by pointing to herself and saying, "There's Carol." Also, Carol keeps things interesting for Amy by changing the activity when Amy loses interest. For example, at lunch, Carol stirs the spaghetti with Amy until she loses interest. Then, Carol changes back to the eating activity. Jeanne makes things interesting by using activities that Amy is known to enjoy. For example, Jeanne found out that Amy liked peek-a-boo when she tried to play it with her. Later, when she wants to make a puppet interesting to Amy, she made it play peek-a-boo. In addition, Jeanne tries to create a positive setting for interaction by being playful throughout the puppet interaction.

Enhancing Sensitivity

Recognize Amy's nonsymbolic behaviors as effective signals.
Focus on Amy's subtle behaviors that signal a readiness to interact.
Respond in a manner that is appropriate to Amy's level of communication.
Respond consistently and reliably to establish her awareness of contingency.

Amy's service providers also know that Amy will be motivated to use more communication if they recognize and promptly respond to Amy's communication in a way that is satisfying to her. In the dialogues, both Carol and Jeanne watch Amy's behavior for actions that appear to be communicative, and then respond to satisfy her. For example, Carol sees Amy look to the diaper changing area before diapering. Carol responds by saying, "Yes! Go change," nodding, displaying a clean diaper, and pointing to the diaper changing area. Later, Amy pushes down on Carol's hands and Carol recognizes this as a signal meaning that she wants Carol to continue patting her diaper with her. Carol responds by patting the diaper with Amy again.

Once in the diaper changing area, Amy begins looking at the shelf where the diapering equipment is kept. Carol thinks that since Amy is looking in that direction, she is indicating that she wants either the talcum powder container or the lotion. She responds by bringing the items closer. When Amy reaches for the talcum, Carol recognized this as a signal, meaning that Amy wants the talcum container. She responds by giving the talcum to Amy. Amy waves the talcum container in Carol's direction. Carol then knows that this means that when Amy does this, she wants to shake the container with Carol because she likes to have her arm wiggled. Carol complies by participating in this activity.

At lunch, Amy reaches for the spoon and Carol recognizes this as an indication that Amy wants a bite of food. Carol responds by giving her a bite. Later, Amy pushes Carol's hand to get her to stir the spaghetti with her. Carol responds by participating in the activity.

During a preschool visit, Jeanne, the speech-language clinician, recognizes that when Amy reaches and vocalizes during the peek-a-boo game, Amy wants her to pop out from hiding. Jeanne promptly responds. Later, Jeanne recognizes Amy's arm waving as an indication that Amy wants to participate in a clapping game with the puppet. Jeanne responds by making the puppet clap.

Increasing Opportunities

Increase Amy's opportunities to communicate by waiting for her to communicate her needs for
    hunger, thirst, comfort, and affection.
Provide consistent time-delays (pauses) during interactions and familiar routines.
Incorporate opportunities that allow Amy to make choices about her needs and wants.

Another strategy Amy's service providers are using to encourage her use and development of communication is to provide Amy with many opportunities to communicate during the day. They do this in several ways. One method they use is to wait for Amy to communicate her needs. For example, Carol waits for Amy to communicate her discomfort at being wet by whining before Carol begins the diaper changing activity. During lunch, Carol waits for Amy to communicate a desire for a bite of food before she gives her a bite, and waits for her to communicate a desire for a drink before giving her sips of a drink. Of course Carol does not withhold food or drink if Amy is just too hungry or thirsty or if Amy is not in the mood to withstand some frustration.

Another method both Carol and Jeanne use extensively to give Amy opportunities to communicate is to provide time-delays or pauses in interactions. For example, at lunch, Carol holds out the spoon and pauses for Amy to signal a desire for a bite by reaching for the spoon. Also, Carol pauses in stirring with Amy to give her an opportunity to communicate a desire to stir. During the play interaction at the preschool, Jeanne makes the puppet pause before it pops out to say, "Boo," giving Amy time to signal that she wants the puppet to pop out. Also, the puppet pauses in shaking Amy's hand to give her the chance to signal for more.

Both Carol and Jeanne give Amy an opportunity to communicate when they offer her choices. For example, Carol offers Amy a choice between the talcum powder and the lotion during diapering. At lunch, she offers Amy the choice of a bite of food or a drink of milk. Jeanne gives Amy a choice between playing a game in which a baby doll puppet zooms in toward Amy's face or a game in which a lion puppet pretends to eat her up.

Sequencing Experiences

Establish routines within daily events to help Amy anticipate what is going to occur next.
Provide opportunities for Amy to participate in turn-taking interactions.
Encourage participation that will increase Amy's social awareness of others.
Utilize patterns in game sequences that playfully involve Amy in a well-defined and easy to
    learn sequence.

Carol and the other service providers know that it is important to organize Amy's experiences into routine sequences so that Amy can become familiar enough with her activities in order to know what is going to happen to her next and to be able to take an active role in the event. For example, in the diapering activity, Carol follows a routine sequence of signaling Amy that she is going to pick her up, picking her up, taking her to the changing table, signaling diaper changing, signaling Amy to take off her pants, helping Amy take off her pants, signaling Amy to take off her diaper, helping her to take off her diaper, and so on until the activity is complete.

Each of the steps is carried out according to a sequence. For example, whenever Carol picks Amy up, she slides one arm under Amy's knees and the other behind her back. Then, she starts to lift and pauses. Because Amy is familiar with this routine, she is motivated to be able to signal Carol to begin lifting her again. She does this by moving her head up. Thus Amy's familiarity with her routine helps her to participate in it.

Carol uses the same method of sequencing her actions to enable Amy to participate in being put down on the changing table, taking her pants down, taking her diaper off, stirring her spaghetti, pouring her drink, and drinking. Both Carol and Jeanne sequence their actions in playful interactions and, thus, enable Amy to participate. For example, Carol plays a game of alternately pushing the spoon and the cup toward Amy saying, "Bite or drink, bite or drink, bite or drink." Carol pauses to give Amy a chance to participate. Amy signals by reaching for Carol's hands. Carol repeats the game and pauses. Amy signals. The repetition of Carol's actions enables Amy to participate in an exchange with Carol. Jeanne uses the same method to enable Amy to participate in exchanges with her and a puppet. For example, Jeanne uses repetition of the actions in peek-a-boo, in a game of zooming the puppet in to pat Amy, and in a handshaking game, to name just a few.

Utilizing Movement

Utilize movements that are matched to Amy's level of actions.

Use movements as communicative behaviors and draw Amy's attention to other people as communication partners.

Select movements that accommodate Amy's ability to interact and modify actions as she communicates within particular contexts.

Respond to Amy's movements as communicative behaviors, increasing the participation of Amy and her service providers in reciprocal interactions.

Finally, Amy's service providers are using movements with Amy to communicate with her and to enable her to communicate with them. For example, Carol uses the joint patting of Amy's diaper to indicate that it is wet. Amy is encouraged to use this same movement to indicate a wet diaper. Carol rocks Amy up a little to communicate that she is going to pick her up. Amy uses a movement of her head to tell Carol to continue picking her up. Carol lowers Amy's legs to indicate that she is going to put her down, and Amy extends her legs to indicate a desire to be put down. She also pushes down on Amy's pants with her help to indicate to Amy to take her pants off. Amy pushes down on Carol's hands to indicate to continue to push the pants down. At lunch, Carol uses putting a spoonful of food into her own mouth, taking a drink of her own drink, and washing her own face to describe Amy's ongoing actions.

In the puppet interaction, Jeanne uses falling back to respond to Amy's action of pushing her away. The puppet uses waving arms to respond to Amy's action of waving her arms. Whitney, one of Amy's peers, uses clapping to get the puppet to clap. The puppet responds by clapping. Whitney uses rocking her head to get the puppet to rock its head. The puppet responds by rocking its head.

Amy Dialogue #1: Diapering

While Carol, the teacher, interacts with Amy during a diaper change, she is careful to match her language to Amy's experiences and expectations. She keeps phrases short, and always pairs them with nonsymbolic expressions that Amy understands and could eventually use to communicate. She moves with Amy whenever it is possible. She uses pauses in moving together to encourage Amy to communicate and to perform functional actions. She is working on encouraging Amy to use taking and manipulating an adult's hands as an all purpose request gesture. Carol responds warmly to Amy's actions and expressions, providing a supportive social context for Amy to develop communication.

GUIDELINES & STRATEGIES	ADULT	LEARNER
Opportunity: Create need for requests	Carol realizes that is is likely that Amy's diaper needs to be changed, but **is waiting for Amy to indicate this.**	
		Amy's eyes follow Carol.
Sensitivity: Recognize nonsymbolic behaviors	**Carol responds by saying,** "Amy's looking." Carol often matches her language to Amy's experience to help Amy attach meaning to words.	
		After a few minutes pass, Amy **starts to whine.**
Nurturance: Expand on child-initiated behavior	Carol **responds by going over to Amy** and saying, "Amy says, 'Come here, Carol.' "	
Nurturance: Focus on individual's interest	Carol says, "I'm here. Hi, Amy." Carol **touches Amy** on the arm and **moves her face** in toward Amy's face to establish social contact.	
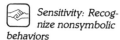 *Movement: Use movements as communicative behaviors*	She **waves** to greet Amy and to model a conventional social gesture Amy could learn to use.	
		Amy **stops whining.**
Sequencing: Establish routines	Carol begins a well-practiced diapering sequence. She says, "Are you wet?" She **slips her hands** under Amy's hands so that Amy's hands are resting palms down on the backs of Carol's hands.	
Movement: Use movements as communicative behaviors	**Together they pat Amy's diaper.** Carol wants to inform Amy of what is about to occur by using this patting gesture and hopes that someday Amy will	

GUIDELINES & STRATEGIES	**ADULT**	**LEARNER**

come to use patting her diaper to indicate a need for a new diaper.

She puts her hands under Amy's so that they can move together without Carol having to manipulate Amy's hands. She avoids manipulation because it often results in aggression or passivity.

 Opportunity: Utilize time-delay

 Sequencing: Encourage participation

Carol **pauses** in patting to give Amy an opportunity to use the gesture. She **keeps her hands** under Amy's to enable Amy to repeat the action without having to search for Carol's hands first.

Amy pushes down on Carol's hands to get Carol to begin to pat again.

 Sensitivity: Respond contingently

Sequencing: Establish routines

Carol **responds by patting Amy's diaper with Amy** and saying, "Amy's wet?"

She continues to the next step in the sequence. She says, "Go change," **shows a** clean diaper, and **points** to the diaper changing area. Carol always uses non-symbolic expressions such as displaying an object and pointing to inform Amy, to help her attach meaning to language, and to serve as models of expressions that Amy could begin to use in the future.

Amy looks to the diaper changing area.

 Nurturance: Provide support

 Sensitivity: Recognize nonsymbolic behaviors

Carol says, "Yes, go change!" **nods, pats** Amy's diaper with Amy, **shows** a clean diaper, and **points** to the diaper changing area.

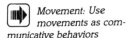 *Movement: Use movements as communicative behaviors*

Carol says, "Up," as she **slides her arm** under Amy's knees and the other arm behind Amy's back, **rocking** Amy up a bit, and **pausing.** She hopes Amy will make a body movement to request going up.

Amy moves her head up.

 Sensitivity: Respond contingently

Carol **smiles and responds by picking Amy up** and saying, "Up."

Carol remembers when she first started

GUIDELINES & STRATEGIES	**ADULT**	**LEARNER**

working in the classroom with a student who did not talk, she would talk constantly. She was trying to do all the talking for both of them. Then, she realized that being a child who does not understand any language is like being a stranger in a non-English speaking country. The streams of words are meaningless. One's only hope of learning to understand is if the speaker uses short phrases and puts the words together with pointing, actions, gestures, and cues from the context. Now, Carol keeps this in mind when she talks to Amy.

 Movement: Use movements as communicative behaviors

 Sequencing: Establish routines

Opportunity: Utilize time-delay

Carol says, "Go change," while **carrying** Amy to the changing area. She **lowers** Amy's legs, and **points** down saying, "Down." She **pauses** to provide Amy with the opportunity to move her legs to indicate down.

Amy looks down and extends her legs.

 Sensitivity: Respond contingently

 Nurturance: Provide support

 Movement: Select movements that accommodate learner's ability to interact

 Opportunity: Utilize time-delay

 Opportunity: Provide opportunities to interact

Carol **responds by lowering Amy to the table** and saying, "Yes!, down," while **lowering** Amy.

Carol repeats, "Amy's wet," while **moving her hands** under Amy's hands and **together they pat** Amy's wet diaper. Carol **pauses** in patting to get Amy to perform the gesture. Again, she **leaves her hand** under Amy's hand to enable Amy to perform the gesture easily.

Amy pushes down on Carol's hands slightly.

 Movement: Use movements as communicative behaviors

Nurturance: Provide support

 Sequencing: Encourage participation

Carol responds by **patting Amy's diaper with Amy** and saying, "That's right, Amy is wet."
Carol **shows Amy a new diaper** and says, "Let's change."

Amy is not looking.

GUIDELINES & STRATEGIES	ADULT	LEARNER
♡ *Nurturance: Focus on individual's interest*	Carol wants to get Amy's attention without being abrupt or intrusive. She says, "Look, Amy," and **puts her finger** in Amy's line of regard.	
		Amy **looks at Carol's** finger.
⊛ *Sensitivity: Respond contingently*	Carol responds, "Yes!, look," **nods,** and **moves her finger** to the new diaper and **taps** it.	
		Amy **follows Carol's** finger.
⧉ *Sequencing: Establish routines*	Carol **shakes** the new diaper and says, "Let's change."	
		Amy is **looking at the shelf** where the diapering equipment is kept.
♡ *Nurturance: Focus on individual's interest* ⬚ *Opportunity: Provide choices*	Carol can't tell what Amy is looking at. She **brings the talcum and the lotion closer to Amy.** She **pushes the powder forward** and says, "Powder?" and **pushes the lotion forward** and says, "Lotion?"	
		Amy **reaches** for the powder.
⊛ *Sensitivity: Respond contingently*	Carol **gives her** the powder.	
		Amy **waves the powder** in Carol's direction.
⊛ *Sensitivity: Recognize nonsymbolic behaviors and respond contingently*	Carol recognizes Amy's signal to have Carol shake the powder container with her. Carol **responds** by **putting her hand over Amy's and shaking the container.**	
		Amy **smiles.**
⬚ *Opportunity: Utilize time-delay*	Carol **pauses** in the shaking.	
		Amy moves her hand to start the shaking movement again.
⊛ *Sensitivity: Respond contingently*	Carol **responds by beginning again.**	
⧉ *Sequencing: Establish routines*	They **continue the game** for several exchanges. Then, Carol says, "Finished," as **she moves Amy through the finished signal.** The signal they use is the action a	

GUIDELINES & STRATEGIES	ADULT	LEARNER

ADULT

baseball umpire uses for "Safe." They perform the action at waist level with palms pointing down. Carol **puts the talcum away.**

Carol knows that Amy does not understand when she says, "Pants off," but she can understand that when she and Carol push down on her pants together it means, "pants off." Carol uses pushing down together to communicate with Amy about taking her pants off. When Amy pushes down on her pants with Carol, she is communicating about taking pants off. Carol uses this resonance method of moving together with her hands under Amy's to communicate about everything they do during the day, including taking the diaper off, eating, drinking, stirring, washing face and hands, drying face and hands, taking off clothes, putting on clothes, obtaining objects, and putting objects away.

GUIDELINES & STRATEGIES

[icon] *Sequencing: Establish routines*

[icon] *Movement: Use movements as communicative behaviors*

Carol continues with the next step in the sequence. She **slips her hands** under Amy's hands, **pushes down** on Amy's pants and says, "Pants off."

[icon] *Opportunity: Utilize time-delay*

She **pauses,** hoping Amy will push down to indicate wanting her pants off.

LEARNER

Amy **looks at Carol.**

[icon] *Nurturance: expand on child-initiated behavior*

Carol **responds** to Amy's focus of attention by **pointing to herself** and saying, "There's Carol." She uses pointing whenever she can because it's an expression Amy could learn to understand if used consistently and one she could come to use. She goes on to say, "I see Amy!" and **points** to Amy.

[icon] *Sensitivity: Respond to individual's level of communication*

Amy remembers the peek-a-boo game they play, and **turns her head away.**

GUIDELINES & STRATEGIES	ADULT	LEARNER
Sequencing: Utilize patterns in games	Carol **responds,** "Where's Amy?"	
		Amy smiles and wiggles.
Sequencing: Provide turn-taking opportunities	Carol **responds again,** "Where's Amy?"	
		Amy looks back and smiles.
Nurturance: Provide affection	Carol says, "Oh!, I see you," **points** to Amy, and **pats** her on the chest.	
		They laugh.
Movement: Use movements as communicative behaviors	Carol **slides her hands under Amy's and together they make a signal for "Finished."**	
Sequencing: Establish routines	**As they make the signal, Carol says,** "Finished playing, 'Where's Amy?'"	
	Carol hopes that the finished signal will inform Amy, and also that Amy will soon be able to produce this signal herself to terminate activities.	
Sequencing: Establish routines	Carol returns to the routine sequence. She **slides her hands under Amy's, and together they push down on Amy's pants.** Carol says, "Pants off." Carol **pauses** to get Amy to push down herself.	
Movement: Use movements as communicative behaviors		
Opportunity: Utilize time-delay		
		Amy moves her hands on Carol's hands.
Nurturance: Provide support	Carol **responds by pushing down on Amy's pants** and saying, "Yes, pants off." **Together they push** Amy's pants off with Amy's hands over hers.	
Movement: Respond to movements as communicative behaviors		
Sequencing: Establish routines	**Carol continues the sequence.** She **points** to the pants and makes **an exaggerated motion** of putting them down next to Amy saying, "Amy's pants." **She uses the exaggerated motion** so that Amy will notice and remember where the pants are when they need them later. Carol repeats, "Amy's pants," and **pats** them.	
		Amy watches.

GUIDELINES & STRATEGIES	ADULT	LEARNER
Sequencing: Encourage participation	Carol **tugs at Amy's diaper** and says, "Diaper off."	
		Amy knows what is next because this sequence has been repeated so often. Amy **tries to pull** the tapes off.
Opportunity: Provide opportunity to interact	**Carol responds by tugging at the tapes** saying, "Pull."	
		Amy **tries to take** the tapes off.
Sequencing: Encourage participation	**Carol holds her hands within Amy's reach and says,** "Help?" She hopes that Amy will take her hands or touch her hands to request help. Carol often offers her hands to Amy when she knows Amy wants help, because she thinks Amy could learn to use hand taking when she wants or needs something.	
		Amy **takes** Carol's hands, **pulls** them down to the tapes, and **vocalizes.**
Sensitivity: Respond to individual's level of communication Movement: Use movements as communicative behaviors	Carol **responds by making a pulling motion over the tapes** and saying, "Amy says, 'Take these tapes off." She often puts Amy's expressions into words and gestures to help Amy learn to understand more communication.	
		Amy and Carol **pull the tapes off** together.
	Carol says, "Rrrrrrrrrrip."	
		Amy **smiles.**
Nurturance: Focus on individual's interest	Carol says, "You like that Rrrrrrip!"	
		Amy **smiles.**
Movement: Use movements as communicative behaviors Opportunity: Utilize time-delay	Carol says, "Diaper off," while **putting Amy's hands** on the diaper, **tugging** at the diaper, and **pausing.** She hopes Amy will pull the diaper off.	
		Amy **pulls** at the diaper.

GUIDELINES & STRATEGIES	ADULT	LEARNER
	Carol **responds by tugging at the diaper** and saying, "That's right, Amy, you pull." She encourages Amy to keep her trying. She **pauses.**	
Opportunity: Utilize time-delay	Again, she hopes Amy will pull the diaper off.	
		Amy **pulls** at the diaper.
Nurturance: Provide support	Carol **tugs** at the diaper saying, "Amy pulls!"	
	Carol knows that Amy doesn't understand her words, but she thinks Amy could learn to understand that when Carol tugs at her diaper she is communicating about Amy pulling her diaper off.	
Opportunity: Utilize time-delay	When the diaper is almost off, Carol **pauses** in pulling and says, "Diaper off."	
		Amy **pulls** the diaper off.
Nurturance: Provide support	Carol says, "Good, you pulled," while **pointing** to Amy and making a **pulling motion.**	
Movement: Use movements as communicative behaviors	Carol has heard Amy's teacher talk about how initially Amy never used her hands for communication or for functional activities. She kept her hands in tight fists. Exercise and massage would loosen them for a moment, but that was all. Carol marvels at how effective teaching the student to use movements to achieve goals is in facilitating the student's physical development.	
		Amy **smiles** with satisfaction.
	The activity continues through their routine sequence of throwing the diaper away, washing up, putting on a new diaper, putting on pants, finishing the diapering activity, and turning to the lunch activity.	

AMY DIALOGUE #2: Lunch

It is time for lunch. Amy is seated in her wheelchair at the classroom table. The teacher, Carol, has heated the food, and placed a bowl of spaghetti and a bowl of pears on Amy's tray. Carol has her own lunch so she and Amy can eat together.

GUIDELINES & STRATEGIES	ADULT	LEARNER
		Amy **leans forward** in her chair, obviously interested in the food, and **reaches** toward the bowl.
Sensitivity: Recognize nonsymbolic behaviors	Carol **responds by extending the bowl of pears to Amy** and saying, "Amy wants to eat."	
Opportunity: Create need for requests	She **fills the spoon** and **holds it** out.	
Opportunity: Utilize time-delay	She **pauses,** hoping Amy will reach for the spoon.	
		Amy **reaches** for the spoon.
Sensitivity: Respond contingently	Carol **responds by extending the spoon to Amy** and saying, "Take a bite!"	
		Amy puts her hand on Carol's and **pulls Carol's hand with the spoon** to her mouth.
Opportunity: Create need for requests	Carol **fills the spoon** again, and **extends it** toward Amy saying, "Bite?"	
		Amy **pulls Carol's hand** with the spoon toward her mouth. She is animated and actively participating.
	Feeding is going so well with Amy actively reaching for and pulling Carol's hand with the spoon to her mouth. Carol decides to try to extend Amy's skills. Up until now, feeding has been done with Amy and Carol carrying the spoon to Amy's mouth together with Amy's hands on Carol's hands. Carol is going to try to get Amy to move on her own to feed herself.	

GUIDELINES & STRATEGIES	ADULT	LEARNER
Opportunity: Create need for requests	Carol **fills the spoon and extends it** toward Amy.	
Opportunity: Utilize time-delay	She **pauses** to get Amy to come for the spoon.	
		Amy **reaches** for Carol's hand, but Carol moves out of the way in time for Amy to get the spoon. Amy **takes the spoon** and **puts it in her mouth.**
Movement: Use movements matched to the level of the learner's actions	**Carol responds,** "Yes, you eat!" As Amy puts the spoon on her mouth, Carol **puts her own spoon in her mouth** at the same time (co-active).	
	Up until this point Carol has communicated with Amy through moving her and being moved by her. For example, when Carol wanted to tell Amy it was time for a bite, she would pick up the spoon, put Amy's hand on her hand and move the spoon toward Amy's mouth. If Amy wanted to communicate a desire to have more food, she would pull Carol's hand with the spoon to her mouth. Now that Amy does not need to be moved through feeding, they won't continue to communicate by manipulating each other. Instead, they will begin to use movements in unison to convey information. Carol will communicate to Amy about eating by taking a bite of her own food, and Amy will communicate with Carol by taking a bite of her food.	
	As Carol puts the spoon in her own mouth, she gets in Amy's line of regard, and emphasizes her movement to draw Amy's attention to the fact that they are moving together.	
		Amy **watches** Carol with interest.
Opportunity: Provide opportunity to interact	Again, Carol tries to extend Amy's skills. Carol **fills the spoon** and **leaves it in the bowl.** She **points** to the bowl and says, "Look, Amy."	

GUIDELINES & STRATEGIES	ADULT	LEARNER
		Amy reaches for the spoon, but can't quite get it herself.
Sensitivity: Respond to individual's level of communication Opportunity: Create need for requests	Carol realizes that this is too hard a task for now. She **extends the bowl** with the filled spoon **and her hand** toward Amy, saying, "Do you need some help?" She **pauses,** hoping Amy will reach for her hand.	
		Amy does not move.
Opportunity: Encourage participation	Carol **extends the bowl and her hand** and says, "Help?"	
		Amy does not react.
Opportunity: Create need for requests	Carol says, "Help?" She **extends the bowl** and this time **bumps Amy's hand** with her hand to try to get Amy moving again.	
Opportunity: Utilize time-delay	She **pauses.**	
		Amy takes Carol's hand and pushes it toward the spoon.
Sensitivity: Recognize nonsymbolic behaviors	Carol **responds by holding out the spoon** for Amy to take, saying, "Amy wants a bite!"	
		Amy takes the spoon, and again they both take bites of their lunches (co-actively).
Nurturance: Provide support	Carol says, "You're doing great!" She **pats** Amy on the back.	
		Amy smiles.
Sensitivity: Recognize individual's readiness for interaction	Carol begins stirring the spaghetti. She notices that Amy is watching her with interest. **Carol responds,** "I'm stirring," and **makes a stirring gesture** by making exaggerated stirring motions with the spoon. She uses the gesture to inform Amy, to help Amy understand Carol's language, and to model a gesture Amy might begin to use. Carol **extends the bowl and her hand** with the spoon, and says, "Stir?"	
Sequencing: Provide turn-taking opportunities	Carol **pauses** to see if Amy will try to stir with her.	

GUIDELINES & STRATEGIES	ADULT	LEARNER
		Amy puts her hand on Carol's.
Opportunity: Utilize time-delay *Sequencing: Provide turn-taking opportunities*	Carol **waits** for a few seconds to see if Amy will try to communicate more. She hopes Amy will move her hand.	
		Amy pushes Carol's hand. Together they stir.
Sensitivity: Respond to individual's level of communication	Carol says, "Yes, we're stirring." Carol **makes bigger motions** when she says stirring to help Amy understand the word by drawing attention to the relationship between the word and the action.	
Opportunity: Utilize time-delay *Sequencing: Provide turn-taking opportunities*	Carol **pauses.**	
		Amy pushes Carol's hand.
Movement: Use movements as communicative behaviors	Carol **responds by stirring** and saying, "Yes, we're stirring." Carol **makes bigger motions** when she says stirring. "Amy helps!"	
		They continue acting and pausing until Amy's attention starts to drift.
Sensitivity: Recognize individual's readiness for interaction.	Carol says, "Eat?" She **holds up a filled spoon** of spaghetti.	
		Amy pushes the spoon away.
Sensitivity: Recognize nonsymbolic behaviors	Carol says, "Finished for now." Carol **puts her hands under Amy's hands** and makes the finished signal. Carol **turns** to feed another student. After feeding him for some time, she offers him a drink.	
		Amy begins to fuss.
Sensitivity: Recognize individual's readiness for interaction	**Carol turns back to Amy and says,** "Amy is fussing."	

GUIDELINES & STRATEGIES	ADULT	LEARNER
♡ Nurturance: Provide affection	**She touches Amy's hand and smiles.**	
		Amy continues to fuss.
♡ Nurturance: Provide comfort	Carol **copies Amy's fussing** and says, "What's the matter?"	
		Amy continues to fuss.
Sensitivity: Recognize nonsymbolic behaviors	Carol **offers Amy the spoon,** "Want a bite?"	
		Amy continues to fuss.
Sensitivity: Respond to individual's level of communication	Carol says, "You want to play?" Carol tries **initiating a clapping game** Amy likes.	
		Amy fusses.
Sensitivity: Respond to individual's level of communication	After several more guesses, Carol says, "Drink?" She **shows Amy her glass.**	
		Amy stops fussing.
Opportunity: Create need for requests	Carol says, "That's it! Drink!" She **holds Amy's glass out.**	
		Amy reaches.
Sequencing: Establish routines	Carol says, "Drink," **as she guides the glass to Amy's mouth.** She takes the glass away when Amy swallows.	
		Amy reaches for the glass.
Sensitivity: Respond contingently	**Carol responds by giving Amy another drink saying,** "Drink." She takes the glass away when Amy swallows.	
		Amy reaches for the glass.
Sensitivity: Respond contingently Opportunity: Provide opportunities to interact	Carol says, "Wait, we have to pour." Carol tips the milk carton over the glass to **demonstrate.** "Help?" **She extends her hands holding the carton and glass** toward Amy.	
		Amy pushes Carol's hand so that it tips the carton up.
Sequencing: Establish routines	Carol says, "We're pouring." (Carol **exaggerates the pouring action** when she says pouring.)	

GUIDELINES & STRATEGIES	ADULT	LEARNER
		Amy reaches for the glass.
Sequencing: Establish routines *Opportunity: Provide choices*	**She holds the glass and the spoon of spaghetti up. She says,** "Drink?" **and raises the glass in a drinking motion, and,** "Bite?" **and raises the spoon in an eating action.**	
		Amy reaches toward the cup.
Sensitivity: Respond contingently	Carol **gives Amy a drink by holding and tipping the cup** for her. **As Amy drinks Carol drinks herself.** As Carol drinks she tries to stay in Amy's view and draw attention to the fact that they are moving together (co-actively).	
		Amy drinks.
Opportunity: Provide choices	Carol **offers Amy the choice again** as above.	
		Amy begins to stare off.
Sensitivity: Recognize individual's readiness for interaction *Nurturance: Create a positive setting for interactions*	Carol wants to get Amy's attention so she says, "Bite or drink, bite or drink, bite or drink," **pushing the spoon toward** Amy on "Bite," and **pushing the cup toward** her on "drink."	
		Amy watches and laughs.
Sequencing: Provide turn-taking opportunities	Carol **pauses** to see if Amy will initiate the game.	
		Amy reaches for Carol's hands.
Sequencing: Utilize patterns in games *Opportunity: Provide choices*	Carol **responds by repeating the show again.** They continue back and forth several times. Then Carol **pauses** to signal to Amy to make a choice.	
		Amy reaches for the cup.
Sensitivity: Respond contingently	Carol **responds,** "More drink!" She **guides the glass to Amy's mouth.** As Amy drinks Carol says, "Drink, Amy drinks."	
		The activity follows in the same way until **Amy refuses** more food and drink.

GUIDELINES & STRATEGIES	ADULT	LEARNER
Sensitivity: Recognize individual's readiness for interaction	Carol responds by taking the bowl and cup away. She **makes the finished sign with Amy's hands** on her hands while saying, "Finished." Carol brings a tub of warm water, two washcloths, and two towels to the table and says, "Wash up." Amy has been trying to wash her face on her own. Amy's independence gives Carol another opportunity to try to use movements in unison with Amy to communicate with her about face washing.	
Sequencing: Establish routines *Opportunity: Utilize time-delay*	Carol **hands one washcloth** to Amy. She **makes a washing motion** over her own face, saying, "Wash face," and **waits.**	
		Amy **tries to wipe** her own face.
Sensitivity: Respond to individual's level of communication	As Amy wipes her face, Carol **makes a washing motion** over her own face with her washcloth and says, "Wash face."	
		Amy **tries to wipe** her own face.
Nurturance: Provide support *Movement: Use movements as communicative behaviors*	Carol **gently assists** Amy. She says, "Yes, wash face. Very good." Carol **makes washing motions** with her own cloth on her own face at the same time Amy moves.	
Sensitivity: Respond to individual's level of communication	Carol says, "Dry, now," and **demonstrates drying with her own towel** on her own face. She **hands Amy** the other towel. She says, "Amy dry," and **demonstrates** again.	
		Amy **swipes the towel across her face.**
Movement: Use movements matched to the level of the learner's actions	As Amy dries, **Carol describes Amy's** action by **copying her movements and says,** "Yes, dry."	
		Amy playfully indicates a game of "Where's Amy?" **by hiding behind the towel** and smiling as she peeks out from behind it.

GUIDELINES & STRATEGIES	ADULT	LEARNER
♡ *Nurturance: Expand on child-initiated behavior*	Carol **smiles and responds,** "Where's Amy?"	
		Amy **hides behind the towel** while Carol says, "Where's Amy?" Amy **peeks out** from behind her towel.
⧉ *Sequencing: Utilize patterns in games*	Carol **responds,** "There she is!"	
		Amy **laughs and vocalizes** excitedly during the game and is quite animated.
⧉ *Sequencing: Establish routines*	Carol says, "Good game! Finished now." Carol **makes the finished signal** with Amy's hands on her hands.	
		Amy **starts to put her towel down** on the table.
▮▶ *Movement: Respond to movements as communicative behaviors*	Carol has anticipated Amy's action and **puts her towel down too , saying,** "Yes, we're finished with that." **She moves Amy through the finished signal.**	
♡ *Nurturance: Provide affection*	Carol **makes a buzzing sound and zooms in and kisses Amy** on the cheek. She says, "You're my girl," and **pats her on the back.**	

AMY DIALOGUE #3: Preschool Visit

Amy's class is visiting a preschool classroom of nonhandicapped students. Jeanne, a speech-language clinician, is working with the entire group on learning the words for familiar actions. They are singing the song, "If You're Happy and You Know It." The speech clinician names movements she knows everyone can do.

GUIDELINES & STRATEGIES	ADULT	LEARNER
		Amy is sitting in Jeanne's lap so that Jeanne can help her to participate.
	Jeanne sings, "If you're happy and you know it clap your hands," and claps her hands. Her hands are between Amy's.	
		Amy likes clapping and is able to push slightly on Jeanne's hands to participate.
	They sing verses including, "Pat your knees," "Stomp your feet," and "Touch your toes." **Jeanne lets Amy rest her hands on Jeanne's to enable her to participate when she can.** After the singing group, the children have their centers in which to go. They can go anywhere they want and play with anything they want.	
Opportunities: Provide choices	**Jeanne holds up a puppet and says,** "Puppets?" as she **points** to the area where the puppet center is, "Or music?" as she **holds up the earphones and points** to the music center.	
		Amy extends her hand up toward the puppet.
Sensitivity: Respond contingently	"Amy wants puppets," **Jeanne says.** Jeanne puts Amy in her adaptive chair in the dolls and puppets center.	
Sequencing: Utilize patterns in games	Jeanne begins playing with Amy. She **covers her eyes, uncovers them,** and says, "Boo!"	
		Amy likes this game and **laughs.**
Sequencing: Provide turn-taking opportunities	Jeanne **begins again** but this time she doesn't pop out right away.	

GUIDELINES & STRATEGIES	ADULT	LEARNER
		Amy **reaches and vocalizes** toward Jeanne to get her to pop out and say, "Boo!"
Sensitivity: Respond contingently	Jeanne **responds by uncovering her eyes** and saying, "Boo!" They continue in the same way for a few exchanges. Then Jeanne tries a different game. She **moves her face toward** Amy's, saying, "Zooom boom!"	
Nurturance: Focus on individual's interest		Amy **pushes her away.**
Movement: Use movements as communicative behaviors	Jeanne says, "Push me away," then she **falls backward.**	
		Amy **laughs.**
	Just then, another child, Whitney, comes over and says, "Please make the puppet do things." This is Whitney's favorite game. 　　Jeanne is not sure if Amy will be able to react to the game, but she decides to give it a try. Jeanne sits in front of Amy and puts on a doll baby puppet. She makes the puppet talk to Amy. The puppet waves at Amy and says, "Hi, Amy."	
		Amy **smiles and moves her arms.**
Movement: Use movements as communicative behaviors	**The puppet mimics Amy.**	
		Amy **watches with interest.**
Sequencing: Utilize patterns in games	**The puppet says,** "I see you. Hi, Amy!" and **zooms in to pat her.**	
		Amy **smiles.**
Sensitivity: Recognize nonsymbolic behaviors	**The puppet says,** "Oh, you like that!" and **zooms in again to pat Amy.**	
		Amy **smiles.**
Sensitivity: Recognize nonsymbolic behaviors *Sequencing: Utilize patterns in games*	**The puppet says,** "Yes, you like that!" and **zooms in again to pat Amy.** Jeanne senses that if she continues with this Amy will begin to lost interest.	
Nurturance: Focus on individual's interest	Jeanne tries a game she knows Amy understands and enjoys.	

GUIDELINES & STRATEGIES	ADULT	LEARNER
▢ *Sequencing: Utilize patterns in games*	The **puppet covers her eyes, uncovers them,** and says, "Boo!"	
		Amy **laughs.**
▢ *Sequencing: Utilize patterns in games*	The puppet **covers her eyes, uncovers them,** and says, "Boo!"	
		Amy **laughs.**
▢ *Sequencing: Provide turn-taking opportunities*	The puppet **repeats the show** and **pauses** before the "Boo."	
		Amy **reaches** for the puppet.
▢ *Sequencing: Establish routines (and) Provide turn-taking opportunities*	The puppet says, "Boo!" **They repeat the game several times.**	
	Whitney, a peer, is delighted with the show. The puppet says, "Hi, Whitney," and **waves.**	
	Whitney **sits down.**	
▣ *Movement: Use movements as communicative behaviors*	The **puppet sits down,** too.	
		Amy is **watching closely.**
▣ *Movement: Use movements as communicative behaviors*	Whitney immediately understands the game and **claps her hands.**	
▣ *Movement: Use movements as communicative behaviors*	The **puppet claps** her hands, too.	
		Amy **waves her hands.**
▱ *Sensitivity: Recognize nonsymbolic behaviors*	**The puppet says,** "Oh, you like to clap, too," and **begins clapping** in front of Amy.	
		Amy **smiles and waves her hands.**
▣ *Movement: Use movements as communicative behaviors*	Whitney tugs on the puppet to get its attention. She **rocks her head** from side to side.	
▣ *Movement: Use movements as communicative behaviors*	The **puppet responds by rocking her head** from side to side.	
	Jeanne **moves the puppet** back over to Amy and continues rocking its head.	
		Amy **watches intently.**

GUIDELINES & STRATEGIES	ADULT	LEARNER
♡ *Nurturance: Focus on individual's interest*	**The puppet says,** "I see you," and **zooms in to pat her on the chest.**	
🚪 *Opportunities: Provide opportunities to interact*	The puppet goes back to **covering its eyes** and **waiting** for Amy to signal it to say, "Boo."	
		Amy **reaches** for the puppet.
	The puppet says, "Boo!"	
	Whitney says, "My turn!"	
	The puppet goes over to Whitney and plays "Peek-a-boo."	
		Amy **watches** closely.
🃏 *Sequencing: Utilize patterns in games*	After a while, the puppet comes back to Amy and says, "Shake hands with me?" and **takes Amy's hand** and **shakes it.**	
		Amy **laughs** because she likes to have her arm wiggled.
🚪 *Opportunities: Utilize time-delay*	The puppet **pauses.**	
🃏 *Sequencing: Provide turn-taking opportunities*		
		Amy **shakes the puppet's hand.**
🃏 *Sequencing: Encourage participation*	The puppet responds by **shaking Amy's hand** and saying, "Yes, Amy shakes hands with me." She turns to Whitney and says, "Will you shake hands with me?" Whitney holds out her hand and the puppet shakes it. The puppet says, "Yes, Whitney shakes my hand."	
🃏 *Sequencing: Provide turn-taking opportunities* ⟋ *Sensitivity: Recognize individual's readiness for interaction*	The puppet goes back and forth between the two girls shaking hands until the game starts to get old.	
🃏 *Sequencing: Utilize patterns in games* 🚪 *Opportunity: Utilize time-delay*	Then Jeanne starts a new game by **bouncing up Amy's arm** and saying, "Here I come to get Amy." She finishes by **touching Amy** on the nose. The puppet **pauses.**	

instead, make use of activities that are familiar to Julie. For example, in the #1 dialogue, Larry uses the movements that are familiar to Julie such as the hand-to-mouth action and the kicking action. Carl and Linda use activities that Julie is familiar with from homelife such as clearing the table, drying the dishes, and folding the towels. They arrange her activities so that they are not too difficult and she can be successful. For example, Larry builds the play activity around movements he knows Julie can do. When Carl and Linda see that Julie is not able to participate in towel folding and dish drying by copying the actions of the adults, they move to make the activity easier and more motivating so that she can participate. When they see that Julie is trying hard in an activity, they enable her to be successful by unobtrusively giving her a little help. Carl pushes her boot on from below as she pulls it on, and Linda pulls the wheelchair the last little bit to help Julie get close to her.

Instead of focusing only on Julie's completing the tasks to a criterion level, all the adults put their emphasis on getting her to participate and to interact with them during her activities. Instead of being directive and demanding that she interact, they make the activities so inviting that she willingly participates. For example, Carl invites her participation in the towel folding activity by providing a motivating game of flying and looping the towel into the basket at the end. Linda creates a positive setting for interaction by playfully "crashing" the dishes into the bin after dinner, and by turning the wheelchair activity into a rousing game of "Here I come to get Julie!"

All of the adults know that Julie likes being wiggled, jiggled, and jostled, so they use movements that will have these effects in order to get and keep Julie's interest. They also watch Julie to see what she is currently attending to or not attending to and use that information as they develop the interactions. For example, when Larry is trying to get Julie to reach, he notices that she is attending when he runs his hand over the tray and grabs her hand; therefore, Larry repeats the action several times. When Carl sees that Julie is not attending to the towel folding activity, he begins a game of tug of war to recapture Julie's attention. Later, after he begins a game of looping the towel into the laundry basket, he sees that he has her attention so he works to get her to fold another towel on her own. After dinner, Linda notices that Julie is looking at the sink. She responds to Julie's focus of attention by saying, "Go to the sink," and pointing to it. During the dish drying activity, Linda tries many different strategies to draw Julie's attention to drying, but Julie just is not interested. Linda noticed this disinterest and cuts the activity short.

Enhancing Sensitivity

Recognize Julie's nonsymbolic behaviors as communicative.
Respond appropriately to Julie's subtle behaviors to increase her understanding that her behaviors can cause desired effects.
Be aware of Julie's willingness and readiness for interaction.

All of Julie's caregivers and service providers realize the importance of recognizing and responding to Julie's attempts at interacting by encouraging her to use her communication and helping her to develop more and clearer behaviors. In the following dialogues Larry is especially sensitive to all of Julie's attempts at communication. For example, when she pulls on his hand as it holds the spoon, he responds by feeding her. When she pushes her head back he responds by rocking her again. He responds to her kicking her leg by bouncing her heels on the floor again. Later, he responded to her reaching for his hand by grabbing her hand and shaking it.

Carl responds to Julie's tugging on the towel to initiate a game of tug of war by participating in the game. He responds to her pushing the towel toward him by beginning the game again. Later, before recess, he responds to her taking the shovel off the shelf by making a scooping motion, pointing to the door and saying, "A shovel to use outside." Throughout the recess activity, Carl is very responsive to Julie's signals. For example, he responds to her pushing the car away by hiding it, and to her reaching for it and vocalizing by bringing it back.

After dinner, when Julie wiggles the cup, Linda responds by bumping the cup with the plate. When Julie pushes on the wheelchair tray, Linda recognizes it as a signal for Linda to unlatch the tray, and responds accordingly. When Julie puts her foot in Linda's hand to get Linda to play a foot grabbing game, Linda complies by grabbing her foot. Later, when Julie wants her mother to continue drying a plate with her, she pushes her mother's hand. Linda responds by beginning the drying action again.

All of the adults who work with Julie know that to encourage positive, satisfying inter-changes it is important to be sensitive to indications from Julie that she is ready or not ready for an interaction with a partner. For example, Larry recognizes Julie's particular readiness for inter-action and takes advantage of it by offering her a whole range of activities around which they can interact. Carl recognizes that Julie is not quite interested in the towel folding activity, so he tries to stimulate a readiness for interaction by folding the towel with her hands on top of his and making big movements to get her interest. Later, he sees that Julie's interest in the game with the car is waning and realizes that he needs to recapture her interest before she will be able to interact anymore. He initiates a game of burying Julie's hand in the sand and searching for it. While Linda and Julie are drying the plates after dinner, Linda is having trouble getting Julie's attention to the drying activity. She tries drying the plate quickly with Julie's hand on her hand to stimulate Julie to interact. When she sees that she has Julie's attention, she continues the game to prolong their interaction.

Increasing Opportunities

Enable Julie to communicate more frequently by providing her with more opportunities for
    interaction.
Provide pauses in familiar activities to allow time for Julie to respond and to encourage her to
    direct others.
Delay immediate assistance to create a need for Julie to make a request.
Provide opportunities for Julie to make choices within daily activities.

Julie's service providers and caregivers are aware of the fact that providing opportunities to communicate and then responding positively to Julie's communication not only gives Julie practice in communication, but also makes her feel more effective and more positive about her interactions with others. This influences Julie to make more communicative attempts. One method Carl uses in order to provide Julie with opportunities to communicate is to offer Julie a choice. For example, when Julie, Carl, and Billy are playing in the sandbox, Carl teaches Julie a game involving pushing a toy car away and then getting it to come back, and a game in which Carl buries Julie's hand in the sand. Once Carl is certain that Julie understands the games, he decides to offer a choice between the two. He holds up the car to indicate the car game and the toy shovel to indicate the burying game. Julie communicates by reaching for the shovel and putting her hand in the sand. Carl plays that game with her, and then offers her the choice again, thus, giving her another opportunity to communicate.

Another method that all of the adults use to get Julie to communicate is to provide pauses in familiar activities. Once a routine is established, the adult pauses in the sequence to give Julie an opportunity to communicate a desire to have the routine repeated or to go on to the next step. For example, Larry pauses in bringing the spoon up to Julie's mouth as her hand rests on the spoon. Julie responds by pulling his hand with the spoon to her mouth for a bite. Later,

Larry pauses in pulling Julie's pants up with Julie to give her an opportunity to signal him to go on. She does this by pulling on Larry's hands. Larry uses pausing in all of the games he plays with Julie such as bouncing her heels on the floor, rocking her back, and moving her head from side to side with his hands to get her to communicate a desire to have these actions repeated. Carl also uses pausing in games to give Julie opportunities to communicate. For example, he pauses during a tug of war game and Julie responds by tugging the towel to get Carl to begin tugging again. He repeats the game several times with the pause to give Julie more opportunities to communicate, and to give him more opportunities to respond. During the sandbox interactions, Carl pauses to give Julie the opportunity to communicate to him to take the car away. She does this by pushing the car away. Linda also uses similar time-delays. She pauses after instructing Julie to begin clearing the table to give Julie a chance to respond by pushing the cup into the bin. Later, Linda pauses in moving Julie's hand toward the cup to give Julie a chance to respond by grasping the cup. When Linda has taken Julie's wheelchair tray partly off, she pauses to give Julie a chance to respond by pushing the tray away. When Linda is trying to get Julie to use her wheelchair, she pauses in moving toward Julie to get Julie to initiate by moving the wheelchair to meet her.

All of the adults give Julie opportunities to communicate by not always anticipating her needs and rushing to meet them, but, instead, letting Julie be aware of her own needs and giving her an opportunity to communicate her need to others. For example, Larry waits for Julie to communicate a desire to eat, Carl allows Julie the opportunity to communicate a desire to get her pants on after a bath, and Linda waits for a cue from Julie before she takes her to the bathroom.

Sequencing Experiences

Organize clear patterns of routines within daily events to develop Julie's awareness of contingent experiences.

Use a calendar of objects that remind Julie of activities and inform her of the routine.

Increase Julie's participation in social, communicative settings by incorporating opportunities for turn-taking.

Encourage simple repetitive games that Julie can become familiar with easily and enjoy.

Julie's service providers and caregivers know that for Julie to learn to understand her activities and for her to learn how and when to perform the actions involved in the activity, they have to be organized in a logical way and repeated. Over time, Julie can show, through her appropriate actions, that she has learned the activity. For example, all of Larry's actions toward Julie are organized into miniroutines in which he provides some action such as moving the spoon toward Julie's mouth, bouncing her heels on the floor, rocking her back, and so on, and then pauses. He repeats the routine over and over again until Julie performs some action during the pause that shows that she has learned the routine. At lunch, she shows she understands the feeding routine by pulling Larry's hand with the spoon in it to her mouth. While rocking back, she shows that she understands the routine when she pushes back on Larry's hands to get him to rock her back again. The actions that she performs not only show that she understands, but they are the behaviors she uses to participate in an interaction with another person. Once she responds to such small routines, Larry tries to get her to learn and participate in a bigger routine. He puts kicking her feet and falling backward together in a sequence and repeats it several times. Then, after he has repeated it, he pauses after kicking to see if she has learned what comes next. She shows that she has learned the sequence by pushing back with her head to indicate falling backward. Again, Larry's use of establishing routines enables Julie to communicate and participate with him. Larry also works to help Julie understand even bigger routines. Every day he shows her the plate that she will use for lunch. He hopes that she will realize that eating will occur after the showing of the plate. Finally, one day, she looks over to the lunch table when he shows her the plate. The routine has enabled Julie to learn when to expect lunch and when to communicate to her teacher about it. Julie can learn to request lunch with the plate or her eye gaze toward the lunch table.

Carl also understands the value of routine and makes sure he organizes Julie's activities accordingly. For example, he has a routine for doing the laundry that takes place before recess. He uses a shovel on Julie's calendar to further signal to her what will occur next. Within the laundry activity, there is a routine of collecting the dirty towels after swimming, taking them to the laundry room, washing and drying them, and then folding the clean ones. Within the action of taking the towel out of the hamper, there is the routine of putting the hand in the hamper, grasping a towel, pulling it out of the hamper, and putting it on the table. Carl is careful to repeat the routines enough so that Julie can learn them, and then provides a pause so that Julie can perform an action in the pause that shows that she understands the routine and that she is able to participate with Carl. Throughout the activity, Carl introduces other routines such as folding the towel and looping it into the basket. Julie quickly learns this routine and shows this by pushing the towel toward Carl to get him to begin the looping action. Later, Julie quickly learns the steps in the pushing game with the car. She shows that she understands by pushing the car away at the appropriate time and, then by reaching and vocalizing to get the car to come back.

In the dialogue between Julie and her mother, it is obvious that a routine is being used. The pattern of taking the tray off the wheelchair after dinner has been repeated so often that now Julie is able to initiate the step by pushing on the tray. Washing dishes after dinner has been repeated enough so that Julie looks to the sink after the wheelchair tray is removed, thus showing that she has learned the sequence. Routines are also evident in the games Linda plays with Julie.

Utilizing Movement

Incorporate movements matched to Julie's level of actions to increase the quality and quantity of Julie's nonsymbolic behaviors.

Encourage playful physical routines that Julie enjoys and can learn to recognize and participate in more fully.

Select movements that accommodate Julie's ability to interact within particular contexts to promote increased use of fine motor control of her right hand and expand her communicative skills.

Respond to Julie's movements as communicative.

All of the people who are involved with Julie know that she does not seem to understand when they talk to her. She watches and smiles when they talk, but does not give any sign that she understands the words. For example, when her teachers says, "It's time for lunch," Julie doesn't try to go to or look toward the eating area. She doesn't even show any sign of being excited. However, when the teacher points to the lunch area and gives her a plate, she does look to the table and smiles in anticipation. Everyone who works with Julie knows they have to make a special effort to get information across to her.

Also, Julie does not use language to communicate. Therefore, all of the adults look for the behaviors that she does use to communicate. One method that they all implement is to use and respond to movements as communications. For example, Larry communicates to Julie about rocking by rocking her. Julie communicates a desire to be rocked by making a rocking move-

GUIDELINES & STRATEGIES

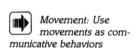

Sensitivity: Recognize individual's readiness for interaction

11–24–87

Julie had her best day yet today. It didn't matter what I tried to initiate with her she would signal for it. **She signalled for kicking legs when she was lying on her back, sitting on my lap, and sitting in the wheelchair. She signalled for me to put my hands over her ears and turn her head from side to side, by moving her head in the pause. She signalled that she wanted more water poured over her hand in the bath by holding her hand out under the faucet. She signalled to have another bite of food by reaching to my hand that held the spoon. She signalled by reaching for my hand to get me to grab her hand and shake it. She reached to take my hand to get me to repeat dragging my fingers down the keyboard.** She did so well today. I hope she can do as well tomorrow.

12–1–87

Julie has been out of school for the last month with upper respiratory infections. She just can't seem to get well.

12–10–87

Julie's been back all week. She has been very cranky. We thought it was just because she had been out so long. We've kept her on her regular schedule. Today her ear drum burst from a severe ear infection. We all learned to look first for medical causes when a student has an unusual and extended period of fussiness.

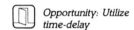

Movement: Use movements as communicative behaviors

1–26–88

Whenever I work with Julie, I **try to keep my hand under hers so that we can move together** (resonance). Then, when I think she understands the activity we are doing, I **pause** to see if she will signal me to go on. For example, today I was putting on her pants after her bath. I **had her hands on mine** as I pulled the pants up her legs little by little. Finally, I **paused** to see what Julie would do.

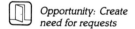

Opportunity: Utilize time-delay

Julie **pulled on my hands slightly.**

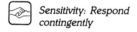

Opportunity: Create need for requests

I **responded by pulling her pants up a little more and pausing.**

Julie **pulled on my hands with more force this time.**

Sensitivity: Respond contingently

I responded again by **pulling up a little more and pausing.**

Julie **pulled on my hands.**

Sequencing: Establish routines

We do all her activities in the same way. It gives her so many opportunities to communicate during the day, and she has learned so many movements and activities as well.

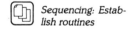

Sequencing: Establish routines

2–12–88

Today when I **showed Julie her plate,** she looked over to the lunch table and **reached and vocalized.** She knows the plate means lunch so we've decided she is ready to have an object calendar. We will start by putting the plate on a shelf in a cabinet. Before lunch we will take her to the cabinet **to show her the plate** so she will

GUIDELINES & STRATEGIES

Sequencing: Establish routines

know it's time for lunch. Then we'll get the plate and carry it with her to the activity. When lunch is finished we will bring it back to the shelf and **put it in a "finished" box near the shelf.** If she shows that she understands that we are using the plate to remind her of lunch by looking toward the lunch area or getting excited like she does at lunch, we can add another object for another one of her activities to the shelf. It has to be an object which she uses during the activity and which will remind her of the activity. When that time comes, we might be able to use her bath toy to communicate with her about bath. One by one we will add objects until there is one for each activity that she does.

3–22–88

Movement: Use movements as communicative behaviors (and) Respond to movements as communicative behaviors

Opportunity: Create need for requests

Julie is doing really well with all her daily living skills. She seems to know most of the movements for washing face and hands, brushing hair, brushing teeth, eating, drinking, and dressing. She **moves her hands with mine as we do these activities** (resonance). Whenever I **pause, she signals me to start again by pushing my hands along.** I think she's ready to start some simple home care activities like dish drying and towel folding. In addition, I think she could begin to do some of her activities without me manipulating her.

4–22–88

Movement: Use movements as communicative behaviors

Today I did a face washing activity with Julie. Instead of manipulating her through it like I usually do, I **got a washcloth** and **gave her a washcloth. I wiped my face with my cloth and pushed her hand** with the cloth in it toward her face to tell her to wash (co-active).

Julie **swiped her face with the washcloth.**

Movement: Respond to movements as communicative behaviors

She understood what I wanted and was able to do it on her own! I responded to her face washing by **moving my cloth across my face** at the same time saying, "Wash face."

Julie **swiped the cloth across her face again.**

I washed with her saying, "Wash face." We continued in the same way for some time.

When I look back to when I first saw Julie, I remember how hopeless and helpless I felt about working with someone with such severe motor impairments. I'm sure I never would have believed that one day she would be able to wash her face on her own, to respond to movements as communication behaviors, or to use movements to communicate with me.

JULIE DIALOGUE #2: Going to Recess

The setting of Julie's second dialogue is in the classroom folding some towels with Billy, her classroom helper, and Carl, the classroom paraprofessional. Carl is using his movements to communicate to Julie what he wants her to do. For example, when Carl wants to tell Julie to take a towel out of the hamper, he begins to put his hand into the hamper making sure Julie is watching him. He pauses in order to give Julie a chance to join him. When Julie begins to reach into the basket, he responds to her action by reaching at the same time. Then, Carl makes sure Julie is watching as he grasps a towel and tries to convey to her to take a towel. He pauses to give her a chance to take a towel. When Julie grasps a towel, Carl begins to pull his towel out as Julie watches in order to convey to her to take her towel out. He pauses. When Julie begins to pull a towel out he responds to her by pulling his towel out. Once they each have a towel, Carl begins to fold while Julie watches, he pauses to signal her to begin, and then folds with her as she folds. Billy is participating by trying to copy Carl's actions.

Julie is starting to become bored with the activity. She is playing with a towel.

GUIDELINES & STRATEGIES	ADULT	LEARNER
♡ Nurturance: Create a positive setting for interactions	Carl wants to see if he can get her involved again, so he **takes hold of her towel**, and **initiates a game of tug of war.** He says, "Give me that towel," playfully, as he **tugs** at the towel.	
		Julie **hangs on** because she likes it when her arm is wiggled by the tugging. She **laughs.**
▯ Opportunity: Utilize time-delay	Carl **pauses.**	
		She **tugs** to get the game started again.
▱ Sequencing: Utilize patterns in games	Back and forth it goes until Carl gets the towel away from her. He folds it and puts it in the laundry basket.	
▰ Movement: Use movements as communicative behaviors	**Carl says,** "Get a towel," as he **puts his hand in the basket.** Billy follows Carl's lead and puts his hand in the basket, too.	
		Julie **puts her hand in the basket and pulls out a towel** with Billy and Carl. She **pushes her towel toward Carl** to get him to play tug of war again.

GUIDELINES & STRATEGIES	ADULT	LEARNER

Nurturance: Expand on child-initated behavior

Sequencing: Provide turn-taking opportunities

Carl responds by **grabbing it** and **tugging it. He says,** "Give me that," as he tugs at the towel. He **pauses** to get Julie to signal to start the game.

Julie **tugs.**

Sequencing: Establish routines

The game goes on until **Carl says,** "Finished playing," and **makes the finished signal.** (The finished signal is like the action a baseball umpire uses to mean "You're safe." The action is performed at about waist level.) He wants to get her to start folding the towels again but he doesn't think she is interested enough in the activity to do it on her own. He decides that she needs some help. He **slides his hands under her hands,** and **folds** a towel (resonance), emphasizing the movements to keep her interest. When the towel is folded, he **takes two corners** of the towel, **gets Julie to take a corner,** and he **moves the towel up and down** a few times and then tosses it in the basket.

Sensitivity: Recognize individual's readiness for interaction

Opportunities: Provide opportunities to interact

Julie **smiles and vocalizes. It is obvious that she likes this game. She takes another towel with Carl and Billy.**

Now that Carl has Julie's attention, he goes back to trying to get Julie to fold a towel on her own.

Opportunity: Provide opportunities to interact

Carl and Billy begin folding while making sure Julie is watching them. **Then they pause** to give Julie a chance to begin folding her own towel.

Julie **begins folding her towel.**

Carl and Billy **continue to fold** (co-active), making sure that Julie is watching and moving with them. Billy likes trying to copy Carl and trying to get Julie to copy him.

GUIDELINES & STRATEGIES	ADULT	LEARNER
		Then Julie **pushes her towel toward Carl.**
Nurturance: Create a positive setting for interactions *Nurturance: Provide affection*	Carl **picks the towel up with Julie's hand on it** and **loops it** a few times before throwing it into the basket. **Carl smiles** at Julie. **He pats her and says,** "You're doing great!"	
		Julie **smiles** and is happy to complete the folding activity now that Carl has made it more interesting.
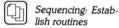 *Sequencing: Establish routines* *Opportunities: Utilize time-delay*	Just then **the bell rings.** Billy **pushes Julie's wheelchair** to within a few feet of her calendar as Carl has directed him to do. Carl wants Julie to move her wheelchair herself, so he is using circumstances like this in which Julie has an expectation and her expectation is not being met. This motivates her to act to put things right.	
		When Julie finds herself too far away from the calendar, **she pushes the switch** on her wheelchair to move closer.
Sequencing: Establish routines	Julie's calendar is an anticipation shelf with one object for each of her activities. The object for an activity is one that reminds her of the activity. The calendar serves to signal her what activity is next. Carl uses it as a context for Julie and himself to communicate with each other.	
Sequencing: Establish routines	Carl comes over and **says,** "Finished folding." He **makes a finished signal** and **touches the towel.**	
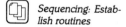 *Sequencing: Establish routines*	"Now," **he says** as he **points** to the shovel. "Recess," and **points** to the door.	
		Julie **puts the towel on the shelf. She takes the next object.** It is a shovel that reminds her of the recess activity.

GUIDELINES & STRATEGIES	ADULT	LEARNER

 Sensitivity: Respond contingently

 Nurturance: Expand on child-initiated behavior

"Yes, Julie," **Carl says as he nods and smiles.** "A shovel to use outside," **Carl says as he makes a scooping motion and points to the door.**

Billy, her friend, comes and takes Julie to the coat rack. He gets his coat.

Julie **reaches for her coat and vocalizes.**

 Sensitivity: Recognize nonsymbolic behaviors

Billy hears her and **gets her coat down for her.** He helps her put it on.

Carl comes over and tells Billy that he wants Julie to wear her boots, because it's damp outside and she may want to get out of her chair.

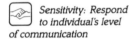 *Sequencing: Encourage participation*

He turns to Julie and says, "Boots," while **pointing** to her boots.

Julie **reaches for the boots.**

 Sensitivity: Respond to individual's level of communication

Carl responds by **bringing them** to her.

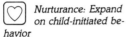 *Opportunity: Create need for requests*

Carl wants Julie to help with her boots. He **holds a boot out** for Julie to put her foot into. Once she puts her foot in, he **drops it** so it hangs on her foot.

Julie **reaches down with her good arm and tugs on the boot.**

Nurturance: Expand on child-initiated behavior

Carl can see she is making a real effort and he wants her work to be rewarded. He **pushes the boot** on from the bottom while she pulls it on from the top.

They do the same thing with the other boot. When they're finished, Carl **smiles at Julie and says,** "Very good!"
  Carl goes on to assist other students.

Nurturance: Provide support

Julie is ready to go out. She **reaches toward the door and vocalizes,** but there is so much noise that Billy does not hear her. She **pushes the**

GUIDELINES & STRATEGIES	ADULT	LEARNER
		button on her tape player, and the tape says, "Come help me, please." She often re- members to use the tape machine when she's acutely aware of something she wants like food, drink, going outside, or rough- house. She never uses it to get help with things that are not very important to her like towel folding and dish drying.
Sensitivity: Respond contingently	Billy hears the machine and **comes over** to push her outside. Once outside Billy pushes Julie near the elevated sandbox.	
		Julie manages to **move her chair** up to the box.
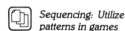 *Nurturance: Focus on individual's interest*	Carl **comes over.**	
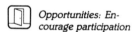 *Opportunity: Provide opportunities to interact*	Billy finds some cars in the box. He **picks one** up and **runs it over the sand** making car noises and **crashes it into the wall** of the box **saying,** "Crash!" Julie **laughs** when the car crashes.	
Sequencing: Utilize patterns in games	Billy appreciates a good audience and **repeats the show.**	
Opportunities: En- courage participation	Carl does not want to interfere so **he quietly moves a car near Julie's hand** that is resting in the sand. Carl would really like to see Julie do something productive or playful at recess because usually she just sits gazing around, banging the shovel on her teeth.	
		Julie **notices the car.** She **picks it up and follows Billy's action of running it over the sand** and **crashing** it into the wall. For

GUIDELINES & STRATEGIES	ADULT	LEARNER
		some reason she finds this hilariously funny and is almost weak with **laughter**.
		They continue the game for some time. Eventually, Julie begins to lose interest.
Sequencing: Utilize patterns in games	Carl joins in now. He **takes a car and aims it** at Julie. **He says,** "Brrrrm, crash!" He **crashes it into the wall right in front** of her. Billy follows Carl's actions.	
		Julie starts **laughing again**.
Opportunity: Provide opportunities to interact	Carl **leaves his car with his hand on it** right in front of Julie. He wants to see if she will signal him to do it again.	
		Julie **pushes the car away**.
Sequencing: Provide opportunities to interact	**Carl responds by taking the car away and saying,** "You push it away!" He **hides** it behind the box.	
		Julie **reaches** and **vocalizes**.
Sequencing: Utilize patterns in games	**Carl responds by bringing the car back saying,** "Julie says, 'Come back!'" He **crashes it** as before.	
Opportunity: Utilize time-delay	He **pauses** again to give Julie a chance to communicate.	
	He remembers when he first started working with the students, he would always do interesting things for them to see and participate in, but he never paused to give them the chance to communicate. He really had to work at remembering to put in the pauses.	
		Julie **pushes it away**.
Sensitivity: Respond to individual's level of communication	**Carl responds by pulling the car away and saying,** "Go away." He always tries to put the students' expressions into words to help them understand more language.	
Sequencing: Provide turn-taking opportunities	He **hides the car again**.	

GUIDELINES & STRATEGIES	ADULT	LEARNER
		Julie reaches and vocalizes.
Sensitivity: Respond contingently *Sensitivity: Recognize individual's readiness for interaction*	**Carl responds,** "Come back! Here it comes. Brrrm, crash!" The game continues until Julie's interest starts to fade. Carl has another idea for a game.	
Opportunity: Create need for requests	**He takes the shovel and covers Julie's hand with sand. He says,** "Where's Julie's hand?"	
		Julie pulls her hand out.
Sequencing: Utilize patterns in games	**Carl says,** "There it is!" **and grabs it and shakes it.**	
		Julie puts her hand back in the sand.
Sequencing: Utilize patterns in games *Opportunity: Create need for requests*	**Carl buries it again.** He says, "Where's Julie's hand?"	
		Julie smiles and pulls her hand out. She looks at Carl.
Nurturance: Provide support	**Carl says,** "There's Julie! I see you," **and pats her.**	
		Julie looks away.
Opportunity: Provide opportunities to interact	**Carl remains quiet.**	
		Julie looks back at him.
Nurturance: Expand on child-initiated behavior	**Carl says,** "There's Julie! I see you," **and pats her.**	
		Julie looks away, smiling.
Sensitivity: Recognize individual's readiness for interaction	**Carl says,** "Where's Julie? Oh, no! Julie's gone!"	
		Julie looks back at Carl.
Nurturance: Provide affection *Sequencing: Utilize patterns in games*	**Carl says,** "There's my girl!" He **pats her** and says, "There's my girl!" **They continue the game until Julie loses interest.**	

GUIDELINES & STRATEGIES	ADULT	LEARNER
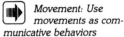 *Movement: Use movements as communicative behaviors* *Opportunity: Provide choices*	Carl decides to offer Julie a choice. He says, "Crash!" as **he pushes the car to the wall and then he begins to bury Julie's hand with the shovel. Then he holds the shovel and the car up in front of Julie.**	**Julie reaches for the shovel and puts her hand in the sand.**
Sequencing: Utilize patterns in games	**Carl buries her hand** and says, "Where's Julie's hand?"	**Julie smiles and pulls her hand out.**
Opportunity: Provide choices	**Carl offers her the choice again saying,** "Crash!" **and demonstrating the crash** or "Bury" **and demonstrating burying her hand. He holds the car and the shovel up.**	**Julie reaches for the car.**
Sensitivity: Respond contingently	**Carl responds by running the car across the sand crashing it** into the wall saying, "Crash!" They continue in the same way until the bell rings. Billy starts to go to Julie's chair to push her into the classroom. Carl knows how disturbing the children find it to suddenly have something happen with no warning so he quickly prepares Julie to be moved.	
Sequencing: Establish routines	**He says,** "Finished playing," and **makes the finished signal.** He goes on to say, "Let's go in," and **points** to the door while Julie watches. He points to Billy as Julie watches and says, "Billy push Julie." Billy **pushes** Julie back into school.	

JULIE DIALOGUE #3: Finishing Dinner

The setting for Julie's third dialogue is at the dinner table. During dinner, Julie's mother, Linda, notices that Julie has not been eating for some time.

GUIDELINES & STRATEGIES	ADULT	LEARNER
Sequencing: Establish routines *Movement: Use movements as communicative behaviors*	She says, "Finished?" She **makes the finished signal.** She **puts her hands in Julie's hands** and **makes a pushing motion** toward her plate to enable Julie to signal by pushing her plate away.	
		Julie pushes the plate away with her Mother's assistance.
Sequencing: Establish routines *Movement: Use movements as communicative behaviors*	Linda says, "Finished." She **makes the finished signal.** She **brings the dishwashing bin** to the table, and says, "Clean up, now." She **makes a motion of pushing the dishes** in the bin.	
Movement: Use movement as communicative behaviors	Linda **begins pushing the plate toward the bin** while **pointing** to the cup for Julie to push.	
Opportunity: Utilize time-delay	She **waits** for Julie to begin pushing the cup.	
		Julie **does not respond.**
	Linda thinks that Julie is not responding because she does not really understand what Linda wants. She decides to tell Julie to push the cup into the bin again only this time, instead of telling her by showing her what to do, she is going to tell her by moving her through the action that she wants her to perform. Linda thinks this will help Julie to understand.	
Movement: Select movements that accommodate the learner's ability to interact	Linda **slides her hand under Julie's** and **moves** it toward the cup.	
Opportunity: Utilize time-delay	Right before they reach the cup, Linda **pauses** to see if Julie will complete the action and put her hand on the cup.	
		Julie **puts her hand on the cup.**
Sequencing: Establish routines	Linda starts **pushing the plate** and says, "Push."	

GUIDELINES & STRATEGIES	ADULT	LEARNER
		This time Julie **pushes, but stops.**
Sensitivity: Recognize individual's readiness for interaction	Linda decides to try to **liven things up** to get Julie more actively involved in the activity.	
Sequencing: Utilize patterns in games	Linda **bumps her plate into Julie's cup** and gives it five or six fast bumps saying, "Boom, boom, boom, boom, boom." Linda pauses.	
		Julie **smiles** and **wiggles the cup.**
Sensitivity: Recognize nonsymbolic behaviors	Linda thinks the wiggling is a signal to bump the cup again. She **responds by bumping again,** saying, "Boom, boom, boom, boom, boom."	
Sequencing: Utilize patterns in games	Now that Linda has Julie's attention she **makes a big pushing motion** and the plate goes into the bin. As she does this she says, "Puuuuuuuuuuuush! Crash!" She **rattles** the bin.	
		Julie **pushes the cup into the bin.**
Sensitivity: Respond to individual's level of communication	Linda says, "Crash!" She **rattles** the bin.	
		Julie **smiles** at the crash. She **looks around** and sees the spoon. She **gets it.**
Nurturance: Expand on child-initiated behavior	Linda **gets the knife and fork.** They **both push** and Linda says, "Puuuuush! Crash!" and **rattles** the bin.	
		Julie **looks around** for more.
Movement: Use movements as communicative behaviors	Her mother responds, "No more. All finished," and **makes a pushing motion** across the tray toward the bin. Linda says, "That was great!" and **pats Julie.**	
Nurturance: Provide affection		
		Julie **smiles.**
		Julie is familiar with the routine and knows the next step. She **pushes on her wheelchair tray.**

GUIDELINES & STRATEGIES	ADULT	LEARNER
⬛ *Sensitivity: Recognize nonsymbolic behaviors*	**Linda responds,** "Julie says, 'Take this tray off.'"	
⬛ *Opportunity: Utilize time-delay*	Linda **unlatches it** and **pauses** to give Julie the opportunity to push it off herself.	
		Julie **pushes the tray off** with her mother's help.
		Julie knows that dishwashing is next. She **looks toward** the sink.
⬛ *Sensitivity: Recognize nonsymbolic behaviors*	Linda **sees Julie's look** and knows Julie is expecting to go to the sink. She puts Julie's expectation into words and gestures to help Julie understand more communication. She says, "Go to the sink," and **points** to the sink.	
⬛ *Nurturance: Focus on individual's interest*		
⬛ *Opportunity: Create need for requests*	Linda wants Julie to use her motorized wheelchair so she **pushes her** to within a few feet of the sink.	
		Julie **pushes the switch on her wheelchair** to move to the sink.
⬛ *Sequencing: Establish routines*	Linda **gives Julie a dish towel** to remind Julie that dish drying is next.	
⬛ *Opportunity: Provide opportunities to interact*	Linda **washes** the plate and the cup and **extends the plate** to Julie.	
		Julie is **playing with the fringe** on the towel.
⬛ *Sensitivity: Recognize individual's readiness for interaction*	Linda **waves the plate** so Julie might catch sight of it.	
		Julie is **still focused on the fringe.**
⬛ *Sensitivity: Recognize individual's readiness for interaction*	Linda **taps the plate** and says, "Look, Julie!"	
	Linda always tries to get Julie's attention without touching her head or face because she knows how touching in this way can make children defensive.	

GUIDELINES & STRATEGIES	ADULT	LEARNER
Movement: Use movements as communicative behaviors	Linda **pushes the plate** toward Julie.	
		Julie take it and lets it sit in her lap. **Julie is kicking one leg.**
Nurturance: Respond to child-initiated behavior	Linda **grabs Julie's foot and shakes it.** She says, "Gotcha! You'll never get away."	
		Julie pulls her foot back.
Sequencing: Utilize patterns in games	Linda **hangs on to Julie's foot as if she were struggling** saying, "You'll never get away!"	
		Julie pulls her foot away.
Opportunity: Provide opportunities to interact	Linda says, "Oops, you got away!" She makes a show of getting ready to grab Julie's foot again and **waits.**	
		Julie puts her foot in Linda's hand.
Sequencing: Utilize patterns in games	Linda **grabs her foot and shakes** it. She says, "Gotcha! You'll never get away!" They repeat the game several times.	
Sensitivity: Respond to individual's level of communication	**Linda returns to the drying activity.** She says, "Let's dry." She **begins drying the cup** when she says "dry." She **holds it right where Julie is looking** and says, "Dry, dry, dry."	
		Julie looks away.
	Julie is just not paying attention to the drying today. Linda decides to give up trying to get Julie to do it on her own for now.	
Movement: Use movements as communicative behaviors *Opportunity: Utilize time-delay*	She **pushes her hands under Julie's** and **picks up the plate** (resonance). She **makes several quick drying actions,** still with Julie's hands with hers, and **pauses.**	
		Julie smiles with the movement she and her mother are making and **pushes her hand to start it again.**

GUIDELINES & STRATEGIES	ADULT	LEARNER
Sensitivity: Recognize individual's readiness for interaction	Linda responds by **making several quick drying actions with Julie's hand on her hand saying,** "Drrrrrrrry."	
		Julie **pushes her hand to start it again.**
Sequencing: Utilize patterns in games *Opportunity: Create need for requests*	Linda responds by **repeating the game,** but then **quickly scoots her hand out from under Julie's** before Julie can signal again. She wants to quit playing but does not want to have to refuse Julie's signal. The game has livened Julie up so Linda decides to go back to trying to get Julie to dry on her own.	
Nurturance: Focus on individual's interest	She tells Julie to dry by **drying her cup in Julie's view saying,** "Dry, dry, dry."	
		Julie **begins drying the plate.**
Sensitivity: Respond to individual's level of communication	Linda says, "Yes! Look at you! You dry the plate!" She **emphasizes her drying motion** when she says "dry" because she would like Julie to understand the word.	
		Julie **smiles,** but she is really **not very involved** in the activity.
Nurturance: Create a positive setting for interactions	**Linda decides to cut the activity short to end on a successful note,** rather than pushing Julie until she becomes frustrated.	
Sequencing: Establish routines	She says, "Finished with the dishes." She **makes the finished signal** as she speaks. Linda is always careful to let Julie know when activities are finished, so that Julie will know what is going on and to give her a sense of order.	
		Julie starts **grimacing and wiggling.**
Sequencing: Establish routines	Linda recognizes this as Julie's reaction to needing to go to the bathroom. Linda **picks up Julie's hand** and **puts it under the front of her belt** saying, "Bathroom." She is trying to teach Julie a signal to use to indicate bathroom.	

GUIDELINES & STRATEGIES	ADULT	LEARNER

GUIDELINES & STRATEGIES

Sequencing: Encourage participation

Sequencing: Utilize patterns in games

Nurturance: Provide affection

Sensitivity: Respond contingently

Nurturance: Provide affection

Opportunity: Create need for requests

Nurturance: Provide affection

Sequencing: Utilize patterns in games

Opportunity: Provide opportunities to interact

Opportunity: Utilize time-delay

ADULT

As she **pushes Julie's chair** to the bathroom **she helps Julie repeat the signal several more times.**

When Julie is finished, Linda wants to work on Julie's use of her wheelchair. She decides on using one of Julie's favorite games to get her motivated to move her chair.

She says, "I'm coming to get Julie," while **walking in an exaggerated manner.** She gets to her as she says, "Julie" and **picks her up slightly** and **jostles her.**

Linda responds, "Get Julie!" as she **picks her up** and **jostles her** again.

Linda knows that Julie will signal again as soon as she puts her down, but she wants to encourage Julie to use the wheelchair. In order to avoid refusing one of Julie's signals, Linda **moves away** before Julie has time to signal again.

"I'm coming to get Julie," Linda sings as she **creeps across the living room, picks her up,** and **jostles** her.

Linda unobtrusively **moves Julie's hand** to her wheelchair switch. She begins the game of walking over to Julie again. This time she **pauses** right before she gets to Julie.

LEARNER

Julie laughs. She reaches and pulls Linda's hands back to get jostled again.

Julie laughs.

Julie is so caught up in the game she fumbles with the wheelchair switch to get to her mother. Her wheelchair moves toward Linda.

GUIDELINES & STRATEGIES	ADULT	LEARNER

Opportunity: Provide opportunities to interact

When Julie doesn't quite get to Linda, Linda unobtrusively **assists by pulling the chair closer.**

Nurturance: Create a positive setting for interactions

When Julie gets to her, Linda says, "Julie!" She **picks her up** and **jostles her.** She **sits Julie back down,** and **puts Julie's hand on the switch.**

Sequencing: Provide turn-taking opportunities

Linda **begins the game again.** This time she **stops** in the same place as before. She is not too far from Julie at all because she does not want to make the task so hard that Julie cannot succeed.

Julie **moves the switch** adroitly and gets to Linda on her own.

Nurturance: Provide support

Linda says, "Julie!" She **picks her up** and **gives her extra jostles** for doing so well.

They **repeat the game** until Julie loses interest but by that time Julie is moving her chair almost all the way across the living room on her own.

Description of Al and Purposes for His Communication Intervention

Al is 15 years old. He is almost totally blind, but occasionally responds to changes in light. He understands several familiar words when they are used within his routine. He communicates only during structured activities when a service provider offers him the opportunity. Outside of structured activities he is content to be on his own and rarely communicates with others. He needs a lot of structure and supervision to participate in daily living skills and work activities.

Al's dialogues occur while preparing for a leisure activity (#1), doing the laundry (#2), and grooming (#3).

PURPOSES FOR AL'S COMMUNICATION INTERVENTION

Developing Nurturance

Encourage the positive relationship he has with the teacher and classroom paraprofessional.
Enhance Al's self-esteem by providing him with plenty of praise and encouragement.
Be aware of Al's interests and use his focus of attention to specific objects or activities as the topic for communicative exchange.
Respond to Al's nonsymbolic behaviors and incorporate these actions as the topic of exchanges.

In the following dialogues, Al's teacher, Andrea, and the classroom paraprofessional, Beth, use several strategies to make Al feel comfortable and open to others and to participate in his activities. Both service providers express their support and affection for Al and their pride in his accomplishments. They try not to be directive with Al. Even when he is engaging in undesirable behaviors such as self-stimulation, they avoid being abrupt and intrusive. Instead, they try to distract him and then gently draw his attention back to the task at hand. They try to arrange his activities so that he can be successful. For example, in the bagging lunch activity, Beth is mindful of the fact that this is a new activity for Al. She helps him through it several times before, then tries to get him to try to do it on his own. Even then, she only asks him to perform the one small step in the sequence that she is confident he can do (e.g., pushing the filled bag down the table). Once he is successful with that, then she tries to get him to perform another small part of the sequence, and continues on until he is able to successfully perform most of the activity. Andrea also tries to make the activities easy and pleasant for Al to invite his participation and interaction. For example, she makes the grooming activity acceptable to Al and invites his participation by making it easy and playful.

Andrea is careful to consider Al's interests in the formulation of the activities to further motivate him to be an active and willing participant. For example, the preparing for a field trip activity is focused around preparing for lunch and swimming, two of Al's favorite activities. The grooming activity makes use of movements Al finds very enjoyable.

During the activities, both Beth and Andrea are watchful to determine to what Al is paying attention and to respond to his focus, if appropriate. For example, when he hears someone walk by the room with a radio, Andrea notices that Al begins to smile and swing his head. She responds to his focus of attention by saying, "You hear the music. You like that!"

Both adults also watch Al's behavior for actions that he displays that they can build a positive interaction around. During the bagging activity, Al touches his mouth to indicate that he wants to eat a chip. Beth responds by assisting him and communicating with him about it. During the laundry activity, Al tries to pull Andrea into the cafeteria. Andrea responds by acknowledging his communication, saying, "Al wants lunch."

Enhancing Sensitivity

Respond reliably and consistently to Al's nonsymbolic behaviors.
Recognize level of Al's readiness for communicative interactions.
Be aware of Al's level of communicative skill and understanding and respond appropriately when conveying information to him.

In the following dialogues, both service providers are very responsive to Al's nonsymbolic behaviors. When Al and Beth are preparing for a leisure activity, Al uses pushing Beth's hand to get her to initiate the various steps in the sequence. Beth responds each time he uses this signal by moving with him to carry out the step. Also, in the laundry activity, Andrea responds and starts the next step each time Al signals the next step in the sequence by pushing or manipulating her hands. In the grooming activity, Andrea responds to his taking her arm by walking with him. She responds to his pulling the soap toward himself by beginning the washing activity. She responds to his rubbing his hands together by repeating the handwashing motion with him. As Andrea helps him wash his face, she responds to his pulling the washcloth to his forehead by tickling his forehead with the washcloth. She also responds to each instance of Al pushing or pulling her hands by performing the actions he requests.

Both service providers know that it is important to the success of the interaction that they try to understand Al and respond appropriately, but they realize that it is equally important to be understood by Al. Both service providers strive to use communication that Al can understand. They both have found that they can use objects in various ways to convey information effectively to Al. For example, Beth uses Al's swimming things to communicate that it is time for swimming. She uses his swimming things and a lunch bag to ask him if he wants to go swimming or eat lunch. Andrea uses the laundry soap and the washer button to ask him whether he wants to pour the soap in or turn on the washing machine. She uses a comb to tell him that it is time for the grooming activity. Andrea and Randy, a student helper, both use patting, tapping, and jiggling objects to communicate with Al. For example, Randy pats the van to get Al to open the van door, and Andrea uses jiggling the laundry cart to request his attention to it. Beth also uses the location of the objects in the bagging activity to cue Al as to what is expected. Andrea uses the natural features of the school to cue Al. For example, she uses his touching the door frame to cue him to enter the room.

In addition to using objects to convey information to Al, both adults use movements to communicate with him. For example, Beth uses moving him through the bagging sequence to instruct him in the actions she wants him to perform. Andrea uses moving Al's hand to the laundry cart to tell him to begin pushing it. Also, both Andrea and Beth use moving simultaneously with Al to communicate with him. For example, Beth gets side by side with Al and begins to rise to tell Al to stand up. Andrea gets side by side with him to signal him to walk with her. She responds to his pulling up on the laundry bag by pulling up on the laundry bag with him. Both adults use pushing his hands slightly to give him a hint of what he is supposed to do next. In addition, everyone who works with Al uses the finished signal with him.

Andrea and Beth are trying to be sensitive to the behaviors that Al displays when he is ready to interact, as well as those that he shows when he is not ready for interaction. They know that when he is engaged in self-stimulatory behaviors such as rocking, swinging his head, and moving his hands as if he were juggling that he is not ready for interaction. They both have several methods they use to get his attention back. For example, Beth gets him out of a sitting position and into a standing position because she has observed that he is better able to attend that way. She also tries to distract him away from stereotyped behaviors by engaging him in a game of patting his hands and getting him to pat hers. Once she thinks she has his attention, she restarts the activity. Andrea tries to get Al's attention back to the laundry activity by jiggling the laundry cart to make a sound he might be attracted to. When he begins playing with the hamper lid, she gently removes it from his hands and restarts the activity. Later, when she thinks his attention is flagging, she speeds the activity up slightly and pauses more often to try to get him more involved in the interaction.

Increasing Opportunities

Provide Al with opportunities to communicate by delaying assistance or removing materials he
   expects to use.
Incorporate consistent pauses (i.e., time-delay) during interactions.
Include opportunities for Al to make choices in daily activities.

Once routines are established, and repeated (as described above under sequencing), a particular step in the sequence can become a signal to Al to begin the next step. Thus, he knows of and can identify the next step. If the teacher pauses at this point in the sequence, Al might be motivated to take some action to initiate the step. In the bagging lunch activity, Beth repeats the sequence with Al's hands riding on hers. When she feels his hands starting to move with hers, she has reason to believe that Al is beginning to learn the steps in the sequence. It is at this point that she provides a pause in the routine in order to give Al an opportunity to initiate the next step in the sequence. Al initiates the next step by pulling Beth's hand as he begins to move the lunch bag. Beth is careful not to implement changes that are too hard or too fast for Al in a new routine, so she tries not to provide too many pauses in the sequence. Instead, she adds one pause at a time and only moves to add another pause when Al has successfully initiated a step numerous times. When Andrea first started doing the laundry activity with Al, she, too, established a sequence, moved Al through it until he started to take a more active part, and then introduced a single pause. Once Al became adept at initiating the step, Andrea added a pause before another step. In this way, she developed the activity to the point as it is presented in the dialogue. Now, Andrea pauses before each step, and, in general, Al responds by initiating the next step in the routine. The activity more clearly resembles a dialogue with Andrea initiating steps and Al responding, and Al initiating steps and Andrea responding. Thus, they each contribute to the progress of the activity through use of mutually understood communications.

Both service providers offer Al choices in his activities to give him even more opportunities to communicate. Beth offers him the choice of having lunch or going swimming. She conveys the option to him by presenting the lunch bag in one hand and the swimming things in the other. Beth is confident that Al recognizes these objects, and knows what they indicate. Al communicates his choice by pushing the lunch bag away, and pulling the swimming things to him.

GUIDELINES & STRATEGIES	ADULT	LEARNER

moves in unison with him. For example, if she wants to communicate to the student to get something like the lunch bag, she would reach for it as he watched. Then, she would pause to give him an opportunity to respond. He would respond by joining her in reaching for the bag.

But, Al is not able to watch and to follow Beth's movements. With Al, Beth has to let him feel her movements for him to be able to "see." For example, if she wants to tell him to get the lunch bag, she puts her arm alongside of his arm, and reaches for the bag making sure he moves with her. When she pauses, he is able to use the same reaching action to restart the motion and, thus, communicate to Beth a desire or understanding of continuing the task.

♡ *Nurturance: Focus on individual's interest*

Once Al is moving well through the bagging activity, Beth decides to try a **pause** before the last step to see if Al will initiate the step. Beth **puts her hand in Al's hand** to make it easy for him to signal by moving her hand.

Al pushes her hand to initiate the action.

⬚ *Sensitivity: Respond contingently*

Beth **responds by finishing the movement with him and saying**, "Yes, push!" When Beth pushes co-actively with Al, she puts her whole arm against his and pushes with him.

⬚ *Opportunity: Utilize time-delay*

They **perform the sequence again** and Beth **pauses** before the last step with her hand in his. She wants him to initiate the pushing.

Al does not move.

⬚ *Sensitivity: Respond to individual's level of communication*

Beth **moves their hands forward** a little bit to give Al a hint. She **pauses.**

Al pushes her hand to initiate the pushing action.

GUIDELINES & STRATEGIES	ADULT	LEARNER
Movement: Respond to movements as communicative behaviors	Beth **responds by joining him in the pushing action** (co-active) **and saying,** "You push."	
Sequencing: Establish routines	As Al progresses in being able to initiate and perform the last step in the sequence, **Beth starts pausing** before the step in which they take the bag of chips out of the box.	
	She chooses this step because it is an easy one, and Al has been actively taking the bag out of the box when they get to this point in the sequence.	
Opportunity: Utilize time-delay	She **pauses with her hand resting on the table next to Al's.** She hopes Al will take her hand to get the sequence going again.	
		Al is not paying attention.
Movement: Select movements that accommodate the learner's ability to respond	Beth **bumps his hand with hers** and says, "Let's get the chips." She **slides her hand forward** slightly to give him a hint.	
		Al pushes her hand to the box of bags of chips.
Sensitivity: Respond contingently *Opportunity: Utilize time-delay*	Beth **responds,** "Good Al. Get the chips." She **pauses** again right before they reach in to get the chips.	
		Al pushes their hands into the box and pulls out a bag of chips.
Sensitivity: Respond contingently	Beth **responds,** "Very good. Get the chips." She continues to **pause** each time at least once before getting the chips, to give Al the chance to direct the action.	
		Al signals that he wants some chips by touching his mouth.
Sensitivity: Recognize nonsymbolic behaviors	Beth **says,** "Chips?"	
		Al starts opening the bag of chips.
Sensitivity: Respond contingently	Beth **helps,** saying, "Open."	

GUIDELINES & STRATEGIES	ADULT	LEARNER
		Al gets a chip and begins eating it.

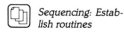 *Sequencing: Establish routines*

Beth **says,** "Al is eating chips." When Al finishes, Beth says, "Finished eating," and **makes a finished signal with Al's hands on hers.** Beth and Al return to the activity.

Now as they go through the sequence, they are pausing before getting the bag of chips and before pushing the brown lunch bag away.

Opportunity: Utilize time-delay

Next, she tries to get Al to initiate the sequence by **pausing** before getting the lunch bag.

Al begins **jiggling his hands** and **swinging his head** during the pause.

Nurturance: Focus on individual's interest

Beth **moves in quickly** to intervene because she knows if this goes on too long she will lose him completely and the activity will be over. She **puts one hand under one of Al's hands and begins patting up on it. She pauses.**

Al begins to laugh and pats down on Beth's hand.

Nurturance: Focus on individual's interest

Beth **responds by patting his hand.** She often tries to distract Al away from undesirable behavior with a game he likes. Once she has his attention, she directs him back to the activity.

Sensitivity: Respond to individual's level of communication

After some time, she **puts her hand in Al's and brings their hands down** to the table. She **makes a slight motion** toward the bag to give Al a hint.

Al pushes their hands to the bag.

Sensitivity: Respond to individual's level of communication

Beth **responds** by getting the bag and saying, "Get the bag." She is careful to use simple vocabulary with Al and to limit herself to key words so that Al will have a chance to learn to understand more language.

GUIDELINES & STRATEGIES	ADULT	LEARNER
Sequencing: Establish routines	It is just about this time that they run out of bags to fill. Beth **takes Al's hands** and **makes the finished signal,** saying, "Finished."	
	Just then, the classroom of nonhandicapped students arrives to help get ready to go on the picnic and to go swimming at the public park and pool.	
	Randy, Al's peer, comes over to see if Al is ready. Beth asks the two of them to carry the box of lunches to the van.	
Opportunity: Provide opportunities to interact	Randy says, "Come on, Al," and lets Al put his hand on his arm. Randy **guides Al to the box.** Randy says, "Here's our box of lunches," and he **guides Al's hand into the box** so he can feel the bags. He **pushes the box** toward Al.	
		Al takes the box.
	Randy stays out in front and **guides** Al as they walk.	
		Al smiles as he carries the box.
Sensitivity: Respond to individual's level of communication	Randy says, "Here we are," and **pats the van.** He stops by the back door. He says, "Let's put it down," and he **begins putting the box down.** Randy has found that if, when he talks to Al, he puts his words together with actions like putting the box down and patting the van, Al seems to understand him much better.	
		Al lets the box go down.
Opportunity: Utilize time-delay	Randy **pats the van** and says, "Let's open the doors." He **guides Al's hand** to the van, **opens the door** part way and **pauses.**	
		Al opens the door.
	Randy **says,** "Good, let's put the box in."	
		Al starts to climb into the van.
	Randy realizes that Al has misunderstood.	
Sensitivity: Respond to individual's level of communication	He comes over and **gently blocks Al's path.** He says, "No, not yet. Let's get the box," and he **guides Al's hand to the box.**	

GUIDELINES & STRATEGIES	ADULT	LEARNER

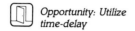 *Opportunity: Utilize time-delay*

The laundry activity is a very familiar sequence for Al, so Andrea **pauses** between each step to see if he will initiate the steps.

However, it wasn't too long ago, when the sequence was new, that Al had to be moved through each part. Andrea had to guide him down the halls, into the room, to get the dirty clothes, to put the dirty clothes in the cart, and to go out of the room. He went along allowing Andrea to manipulate him passively, but he did not participate. Gradually, after time, Al did begin to participate.

Finally, the day came when Andrea could pause before one step in the sequence and Al would initiate it. For example, she paused before putting the dirty clothes into the cart and Al took her hand, put it on the dirty clothes, and lifted them into the cart. And gradually, week after week, Andrea added pauses before each of the steps to encourage Al to participate and communicate more during the activity.

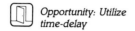 *Opportunity: Provide opportunities to interact*

Andrea **waits** for Al to make the next move.

Al tries to pull the laundry cart into the room.

♡ *Nurturance: Provide support*

Andrea **goes with him** saying, "Go in!"

Sequencing: Establish routines

Al and Andrea push the laundry cart as before until it bumps into the hamper in the room. Andrea tries to use each object Al touches as a cue to Al to perform the next step in a sequence.

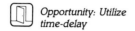 *Opportunity: Provide opportunities to interact*

Andrea **pauses** to see what Al will do.

Al does nothing. He begins rocking his head.

♡ *Nurturance: Focus on individual's interest*

Andrea intervenes quickly because she knows if he gets too involved with rocking, he becomes very inattentive. She **jig-**

GUIDELINES & STRATEGIES	ADULT	LEARNER
	gles the laundry cart and says. "Here we are," to get his attention and to get him involved again.	
		He still does not act.
🔊 *Movement: Use movements as communicative behaviors* 🚪 *Opportunity: Utilize time-delay*	Andrea **moves Al's hand slightly** to give him a hint to begin to trail around the laundry cart to get the classroom hamper. She **waits.**	
		Al takes Andrea's hand and **pushes it around** the frame of the laundry bag.
🔊 *Movement: Respond to movements as communicative behaviors* 📑 *Sequencing: Establish routines*	Andrea **responds by moving with him and saying,** "Yes, let's go find the laundry." Andrea lets Al trail around until his hand bumps into the hamper.	
		Al takes the lid off the hamper and begins to jiggle it.
♡ *Nurturance: Focus on individual's interest*	Again, Andrea **moves quickly** to intervene. She wants to get the lid away from him, but without being intrusive or abrupt.	
♡ *Nurturance: Create a positive setting for interactions*	She says, "Give me the lid," and **gently removes it** from Al's hands. The lid has always been a problem. She reminds herself to work on the hampers that afternoon to make the lids open, but not come off.	
♡ *Nurturance: Focus on individual's interest* 🚪 *Opportunity: Create need for requests*	She **jiggles the hamper** to try to get Al back to the task. She **waits** to see what he'll do.	
		Al starts gathering up the plastic bag within the hamper in order to take it out.
🔊 *Movement: Use movements matched to the level of the learner's actions* 🚪 *Opportunity: Utilize time-delay*	Andrea **puts her hands touching Al's and follows his movements.** Once the bag is gathered up she **pauses, leaving her hand next to his.** She often uses this method of putting her hand on or near his so that he can take	

GUIDELINES & STRATEGIES	ADULT	LEARNER
	her hand or push her hand to signal her to do something.	
		Al makes a pulling up action bumping Andrea's hands.
Movement: Respond to movements as communicative behaviors *Sensitivity: Respond to individual's level of communication*	Andrea says, "Yes, take it out," and **moves with him to take it out.** Andrea **guides it** until it's over the laundry cart. She **shakes the laundry cart** to let him know where it is.	
		Al lets the plastic bag go into the laundry cart.
Movement: Use movements matched to the level of the learner's actions *Nurturance: Provide support* *Opportunity: Utilize time-delay*	Andrea **keeps her hands next to his and moves as he does** saying, "We put it in." She **pats him** and says, "Good job." She **pauses.**	
		Al puts his hands on the laundry cart, but realizes Andrea is not with him. He reaches over and takes her hand to put it in position on the cart so that they can leave the room.
	Andrea says, "Come here, Andrea." She often speaks for Al, putting his expressions into words, to help him learn to understand her words.	
		Al begins pushing.
Movement: Respond to movements as communicative behaviors	**Andrea responds** by **moving forward with him** saying, "Yes, let's go." When they get outside Andrea stops and says, "Stop. Lisa's turn." She gets Al over to the wall so he can trail to the next room. Then she attends to Lisa.	
	Although there are two students involved in the laundry activity, Andrea works with them individually, first with one, then with the other. She does this because neither one of them either attends to or partici-	

GUIDELINES & STRATEGIES	ADULT	LEARNER
	pates in the activity unless Andrea is concentrating her entire effort on getting him or her to attend and interact. If Andrea is paying attention to Al, Lisa simply begins self-stimulating and disregards the others. If Andrea pays attention to Lisa, Al reverts into self-stimulation.	
		Al is rocking and jiggling his head.
♡ *Nurturance: Focus on individual's interest*	When it is time for Al's turn again, he is so involved with rocking his head and jiggling his hands that Andrea realizes it is going to be a problem to get him involved again. She tries distracting him out of it by starting a game of patting up on his downturned palms. Sometimes this game works to draw his attention back to Andrea.	
▢ *Sequencing: Utilize patterns in games*	**As she pats his hands she says,** "Pat, pat, pat," in a playful way. **She repeats,** "Pat, pat, pat," **and pats his hands several times.**	
▢ *Opportunity: Utilize time-delay*	She **pauses.**	
		Al smiles and pats back.
▢ *Sequencing: Provide turn-taking opportunities*	**Andrea pats Al's hands** and says, "You like that." She **pauses.**	
		Al smiles and pats her hands.
▢ *Sequencing: Establish routines*	After a few times, Andrea thinks she has Al's attention so she directs him back to the laundry task, "Finished playing," she says, and **makes the finished signal with his hands on her hands.** She moves him quickly back to the laundry task to prevent him from lapsing into self-stimulation again.	
⏩ *Movement: Select movements that accommodate the learner's ability to interact* ▢ *Opportunity: Provide opportunities to interact*	She **slides her hand under his and guides it to the cart.** She says, "Push," and **begins pushing the cart.** This time she **pauses** more frequently while they are walking because she knows that pausing not only encourages Al to communicate,	

GUIDELINES & STRATEGIES	**ADULT**	**LEARNER**
	it keeps him more active and attentive as they walk.	
		As they walk past the cafeteria, Al hears the dishes rattling and smells the food. **He takes Andrea's hand and tries to pull her into the cafeteria.**
Sensitivity: Respond contingently	**Andrea says,** "Al wants lunch. No lunch. Laundry." She guides Al's hands back to the cart.	
	Al, Andrea, and Lisa continue until all the laundry is collected. Then, Al and Andrea push the laundry cart down the hall until they get to the laundry room.	
Opportunity: Utilize time-delay	Andrea says as before, "Push, push, push, push, stop!" and **pauses.**	
		Al signals her to move again each time by **pulling her hand forward.**
Sequencing: Establish routines	Once in the laundry room, Andrea says, "Here we are," and **bumps the laundry cart into the washing machine.** Andrea hopes that the sound and feel of bumping into the washing machine together with the smells and other features of the room will cue Al that he is in the laundry room.	
Opportunity: Provide opportunities to interact	Andrea **pauses** to see what Al will do.	
		Al nudges her to move around the cart to the washer.
Sensitivity: Respond to individual's level of communication *Nurturance: Expand on child-initiated behavior*	Andrea **puts his expression into words** by saying, "Go to the washer." She lets him bump his hand into the washer. She says, "There's the washer." She **pats the lid** to get him to put his hand on it. She says, "Open."	
		Al puts his hand on it.
Opportunity: Provide opportunities to interact	**Andrea puts her hand next to Al's and begins to open the lid. She pauses.**	

GUIDELINES & STRATEGIES	**ADULT**	**LEARNER**
		Al responds by pulling on the lid.

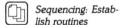 *Movement: Use movements matched to the level of the learner's actions*

Andrea keeps her hand touching Al's and co-actively they open the lid.

Andrea always moves with Al. They walk, push, open, pick up, put down, sit, and stand together. Andrea uses a movement like walking to communicate to Al to walk. He can respond to her expression by walking. Al can use the action of walking to communicate to Andrea that he wants to walk. Andrea responds by walking. Thus, it is through these movements that they communicate with each other.

Opportunity: Utilize time-delay

As they open the lid, Andrea says, "That's right, open." She **leaves her hand next to his** and **pauses** to see what Al will do. She hopes he will take her hand and push it to the laundry cart to initiate taking the dirty things out of the cart.

He does not move.

Movement: Select movements that accommodate the learner's ability to interact

When Al does not initiate taking the dirty things out, Andrea **does by sliding her hand under Al's, guiding it to a plastic bag in the cart, and saying,** "Take out."

Al grasps the bag and pulls it out.

Movement: Use movements matched to the level of the learner's actions

Andrea **guides Al's hands** to the bottom of the bag and they dump the dirty clothes into the washer.

Sequencing: Establish routines

Andrea says, "Finished for now, Al," and **makes a finished sign with him.** She says, "It's Lisa's turn."

Andrea is always careful to try to keep Al informed of what is going on because she does not want to confuse him. She knows how disturbing it can be to be confused. Andrea turns and works with Lisa while Al waits. When she's finished with Lisa she returns to Al. She offers Al a choice to give him an opportunity to communicate.

GUIDELINES & STRATEGIES	ADULT	LEARNER

 Opportunity: Provide choices

She **says to Al,** "Soap? or button?" When she says, "Soap" **she puts the measuring cup in his hand.** When she says, "Button?" **she puts his other hand on the "on" button on the washing machine.**

Al is familiar with pouring the soap in and pulling the "on" button because he has done this activity so many times before. He **chooses pulling the "on" button. He communicates this by pushing the measuring cup away and turning toward the washer.**

Al **pulls the button out.** He smiles when he hears the water coming into the washer.

Andrea **says,** "You pulled the button."

Andrea lets him feel the water coming in. She says, "Water. Wash the clothes." Then, she says, "Finished for now," and **makes the finished signal with Al's hands** on her hands while Lisa watches. Then, they go on to their next activity. They'll come back to the laundry later.

Sequencing: Establish routines

AL DIALOGUE #3: Grooming

Al is near other classmates in a recreation area in the school building. Al has been playing with a keyboard during his free time before school begins. When the bell rings, Andrea, his teacher, comes over to where he is sitting.

GUIDELINES & STRATEGIES	ADULT	LEARNER
Sequencing: Establish routines	Andrea **says,** "Finished, Al," and **slides her hands under his to make the finished signal.**	
		Al does not get up.
Nurturance: Focus on individual's interest *Sequencing: Establish routines*	Andrea **gets down at his level, pats her arm,** and **touches her arm to Al's,** the signal for him to go with her.	
		Al takes her arm and gets up.
Movement: Use movements matched to the level of the learner's actions	Andrea **rises with him and says,** "Yes, stand up." Andrea always tries to use movement to communicate with him because Al can understand and respond to movements as communications, whereas he has considerable difficulty in understanding and responding to language.	
		Al forgets to take the keyboard.
Opportunity: Provide opportunities to interact *Sequencing: Encourage participation*	Andrea **plays a note** to remind him. When he does not move, she **moves her arm down his arm** to indicate that she wants him to move with her.	
		Al and Andrea pick up the keyboard together. He takes it under his arm. Then, he takes Andrea's arm.
Opportunity: Utilize time-delay	Andrea **says,** "Good. Let's go to the calendar." When they get to the calendar, Andrea says, "Finished with the keyboard." She **pauses** to let Al find the finished box.	
		Al does not move.
Sequencing: Establish routines	Andrea **pats the finished box and says,** "Finished with the keyboard." Andrea is using the shelf to communicate with Al about his activities. Therefore, when she communicates with Al at the shelf, she	

GUIDELINES & STRATEGIES	ADULT	LEARNER
	limits her topics to the activity that is finished and the activity that is coming up. She avoids turning the focus of conversation to how to work the shelf by refraining from communicating about putting in, taking out, and finding the right cubby hole.	
		Al hears Andrea pat the box. He **puts the keyboard away.**
	Andrea **says**, "Yes, finished with the keyboard, now. . .?" She **pats the cubby hole containing the object for the next activity.**	
		Al reaches into the next cubby hole and gets the comb.
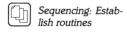 Movement: Use movements as communicative behaviors	Andrea **says**, "Now grooming," and **slides her hand under Al's.** She **moves their hands up to his head** to touch the comb to his hair. She hopes that someday he will use this action as a signal to initiate	
Opportunity: Utilize time-delay	the grooming activity. She **waits** to see if he will initiate going over to the sink.	
		Al takes her arm and pushes slightly.
Sensitivity: Respond to individual's level of communication	Andrea **responds**, "Let's go," and she **begins walking.**	
	Andrea looks forward to and at the same time dreads grooming with Al. It is her greatest challenge. He does not like grooming and can be very difficult. She persists in having a grooming activity because he needs to acquire the skills. Her goal is to get him to like the activities so that he will learn grooming skills. She uses the comb to signal grooming because, oddly enough, combing is the only part of the activity Al really likes.	
		When they get to the sink Al **begins combing his hair.**
Sequencing: Establish routines	Andrea likes to save combing for last to provide Al with something to look forward to. She **says**, "Let's put the comb down," and **pats the counter.**	

GUIDELINES & STRATEGIES	ADULT	LEARNER
	It is hard for Andrea, at times like this, to avoid just taking the comb away or manipulating Al to put it down, but she knows it's better for him to learn to act and respond more independently.	
		Al puts the comb down.
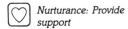 *Nurturance: Provide support*	Andrea **says,** "Very good!" She **pats him on the back.** She gives a lot of encouragement during grooming because she knows how difficult it is for him. A lot of the activity is done in resonance to keep it fun and easy.	
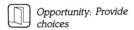 *Opportunity: Provide choices*	Andrea begins the activity by giving Al a choice. **She says,** "Wash hands or wash face?" When she says, "Wash hands?" **she puts the bar of soap in his left hand.** When she says, "Wash face?" **she puts the washcloth in the other hand.**	
		Al is familiar with these objects and the actions they are associated with because he has done this activity so many times before. Al pulls the soap to him and pushes the washcloth back to Andrea.
Sensitivity: Recognize nonsymbolic behaviors	Andrea **says,** "Wash hands. OK."	
Movement: Select movements that accommodate the learner's ability to respond	Andrea **slides her hand under Al's** and **moves their hands to turn on the water** (resonance).	
		Al puts his hands under the water and starts moving his hands as if he were juggling.
Nurturance: Focus on individual's interest	Andrea **moves in quickly** to stop him before he gets too involved in self-stimulation. She **begins the washing activity.**	

GUIDELINES & STRATEGIES	ADULT	LEARNER
♡ *Nurturance: Create a positive setting for interactions*	Al does not like having the soap on his hands, so Andrea begins by **lathering her hands with Al's hands resting on hers.**	
▯ *Opportunity: Utilize time-delay*	She **puts the soap down and rubs her hands together quickly with Al's hands still on hers.** She thinks he may like the movement. She **pauses** to see if he will try to start it again.	
		Al smiles and makes a humming sound. He pushes her hands to get her to begin again.
🤝 *Sensitivity: Respond contingently* ▯ *Opportunity: Utilize time-delay*	Andrea responds by **rubbing her hands together** quickly with Al's hands resting on hers as before. She **pauses.**	
		Al pushes her hands.
🤝 *Sensitivity: Recognize individual's readiness for interaction*	Andrea responds by beginning the **lathering action** again. By this time, there is some soap on Al's hands but either he has not noticed or he does not care.	
♡ *Nurturance: Focus on individual's interest*	Andrea **turns her hands so that they are palms up.** Al's hands are now on top of hers, palms down. Andrea **moves to rub Al's hands** quickly before he gets a chance to realize that he is getting soapy and starts to complain.	
		Al likes the action and smiles.
▯ *Opportunity: Utilize time-delay*	Andrea **pauses.**	
		Al moves his hands over hers to signal to go again.
🤝 *Sensitivity: Respond contingently*	Andrea responds by **moving her hands quickly under his.** They continue a few more times. Andrea acts, then pauses. Al signals, then Andrea acts and pauses. Things are going so well Andrea decides to try to get Al to rub his hands together.	
♡ *Nurturance: Create a positive setting for interaction*	She **takes his wrists, puts his hands together,** and **makes them rub together** in a fast rubbing motion. **She sings,** "Rub-	

GUIDELINES & STRATEGIES	ADULT	LEARNER
	bing, rubbing, rubbing," to distract him and keep him from becoming upset.	
		Al pushes his hands apart.
Sequencing: Utilize patterns in games	Andrea lets his hands separate. She decides to try another approach. She **moves his hands in the rubbing motion** while they are apart, **gradually she pushes them together** for a brief rubbing together, and then she **pulls them apart** and **pauses.**	
		Al moves his hands toward her to get her to begin again.
Sequencing: Provide turn-taking opportunities	Andrea **repeats the new game** and **pauses.**	
		Al moves his hands to signal her to start.
	They continue as before, but each time Andrea lengthens the time he is rubbing his hands together.	
Sequencing: Establish routines	Finally, Andrea **goes back to rubbing his hands together quickly.** She **pauses** holding his hands together.	
		Al rubs his hands together to signal her to start the rubbing action again.
Sensitivity: Respond contingently *Nurturance: Provide support*	Andrea responds by **rubbing his hands together, and by saying,** "Yes! You wash your hands." They continue in this way through several exchanges.	
Nurturance: Provide support	Each time Al rubs his hands together for a longer period and Andrea **gives him a lot of praise and encouragement.**	
Nurturance: Create a positive setting for interactions	When they are finished, Andrea **says,** "Very good," and further rewards him by **letting him hold his hands under the faucet** for a minute before going on to face washing.	

GUIDELINES & STRATEGIES	**ADULT**	**LEARNER**

 Movement: Use movements as communicative behaviors

 Sequencing: Establish routines

 Sequencing: Establish routines

Andrea **slides her hands under Al's** and says, "Finished rinsing," and **helps him make the finished signal** (resonance).

She **says,** "Let's get the washcloth," and **begins moving their hands to the place where the washcloth is kept.**

Just then, somebody walks by the room carrying a radio.

Al smiles and begins swinging his head when he hears the music.

 Nurturance: Focus on individual's interest

Andrea **says,** "You hear the music. You like that!" The music fades and Andrea returns to the activity.

 Movement: Use movements as communicative behaviors

She **gets the washcloth wet while Al's hands ride on hers** (resonance).

 Nurturance: Focus on individual's interest

 Nurturance: Create a positive setting for interactions

She **moves around so she is in front of him.** She keeps her hands under his. She **touches him on the chin** and says, "Wash here," and then **tickles his chin with the cloth** as they wash it.

She has found that Al is much less defensive and more cooperative if she touches the place where they are going to wash before they wash it. She goes on in the same way to do his cheek and his nose. Finally, she touches him on the other cheek, moves the cloth close to his face, and **pauses.**

 Sequencing: Establish routines

 Opportunity: Utilize time-delay

Al pulls the cloth to his face.

 *Nurturance: Provide affection*

Andrea **responds by tickling him on the forehead** as they wash it. They continue this way until his face is washed.

Her next step will be to pull her hand away at the last second as Al pulls the cloth to his face. Then, she'll give him a lot of praise and encouragement for doing it on his own. Gradually, Al will do more and more until he's washing himself independently.

GUIDELINES & STRATEGIES	ADULT	LEARNER
	But, for now, Andrea is glad he accepts as much contact with the washcloth as he does. They dry his face in the same way.	
	Finally, they get to brushing teeth. Al has always been so difficult when brushing his teeth that everyone has avoided doing it. As a result, his mouth is in terrible shape. Andrea has been trying to get him to be more accepting of the toothbrush by being very gentle and totally responsive to his communications that indicate a desire to stop.	
Movement: Use movements as communicative behaviors *Sequencing: Establish routines*	Andrea **says,** "Brush teeth," **slides her hand under his,** and **moves their hands to the place where the tooth brush** is always kept (resonance).	
	Andrea thinks it is just as important to give the students the bad news as it is to give them the good news.	
Sequencing: Encourage participation	Andrea **puts the paste on the brush.** She **holds it in front of his mouth.** She **keeps his hand resting on her hand** to enable him to signal whenever needed.	
		Al immediately pushes her hand away.
Sensitivity: Recognize individual's readiness for interaction	Andrea **responds by retracting her hand for a moment.** Then **she puts the brush back up** by his mouth **saying,** "Here it comes."	
		Al pushes her hand away.
Sensitivity: Recognize individual's readiness for interaction *Opportunity: Create needs for requests*	Andrea **retracts her hand** and **waits for a moment.** The exchange continues in the same way until Al does not push away. Then Andrea does a **quick brushing motion** with the back of the toothbrush on his lips **saying,** "Brush, brush, brush." She **pulls the brush away.**	
		Al **pulls her hand back** to let her to do it again.

GUIDELINES & STRATEGIES	ADULT	LEARNER
Sensitivity: Respond contingently *Sequencing: Provide turn-taking opportunities*	Andrea **responds by repeating the brushing action** on his lips. **They continue in the same way for several exchanges.**	
		Al **opens his mouth to taste the toothpaste.**
Sensitivity: Recognize individual's readiness for interaction *Opportunity: Create needs for requests*	Andrea **moves quickly to put the brush in his mouth.** **She pulls her hand away** to give him a chance to ask her to do it. She has found that the students really drop their defenses when she can get them to ask for what she wants to do.	
		Al **laughs and pulls her hand back to his mouth.**
Sensitivity: Respond contingently *Opportunity: Create needs for requests*	Andrea **responds by putting the brush in his mouth and pulling it away.** She **waits.**	
		Al **pulls the brush back and opens his mouth.**
Sensitivity: Recognize individual's readiness for interaction *Opportunity: Create need for requests*	Andrea **brushes some of his teeth quickly and pulls the brush away.**	
		Al **opens his mouth. He pulls the brush into his mouth.**
Sensitivity: Respond contingently *Opportunity: Create need for requests*	Andrea **brushes some of his teeth.** She only stays in his mouth for a few seconds each time so that Al won't be too overwhelmed and he will be motivated to ask for more. Andrea **pulls her hand away.**	
		Al **opens his mouth and pulls the brush into his mouth.**
Nurturance: Expand on child-initiated behavior	Andrea responds by brushing **some of his teeth and pulling away.** The activity continues until Andrea senses that to go on longer would be pushing Al too far. She	

GUIDELINES & STRATEGIES	ADULT	LEARNER
	hopes that tomorrow they will begin where they left off with Al opening his mouth for the toothbrush.	
♡ *Nurturance: Create a positive setting for interactions*	Andrea **says,** "OK, now comb!"	
		Al hears one of his favorite words and reaches around until he finds the comb. He **happily combs his hair.**

◀ JENNIFER ▶

Description of Jennifer and
Purposes for Her Communication Intervention

Jennifer is 14 years old. She understands very little language, and rarely tries to communicate. When she does try to communicate, she uses pushing away and hitting to communicate a desire to be left alone. She is highly defensive, and can be aggressive with adults when they try to interact with her.

She manages her own personal hygiene and self-care needs. She can also perform activities of daily life such as simple food preparation, laundry, house cleaning, and dishwashing with moderate supervision.

Jennifer's dialogues occur during an interaction with her teacher, Wendy (#1), during physical therapy in an exercise activity (#2), and during a week-long shopping and baking activity (#3).

PURPOSES FOR JENNIFER'S COMMUNICATION INTERVENTION

Developing Nurturance

Create a positive atmosphere for Jennifer by respecting her low tolerance to being touched.
Emphasize activities in which Jennifer shows interest in order to accommodate her preferences
    and to expand on her initiated behaviors.
Develop a warm, secure relationship with Jennifer to promote an atmosphere that encourages
    positive interactions.

In the following dialogues, Jennifer's teacher, Wendy, dedicates herself to developing a positive relationship with Jennifer. This is difficult with Jennifer because she is so defensive to any overture from another person. Wendy believes that Jennifer is so defensive because she feels that she lacks control of interactions with another person. Wendy suspects that in the past others have regarded Jennifer's behavior as acts of defiance and have responded by punishing her. As a result, Jennifer has felt less in control and has become more defensive and more aggressive. A vicious cycle has developed that has left Jennifer completely closed to others. She has become so defensive that even the most innocuous action on the part of the adult can incite her to act aggressively. She has been known to chase a teacher down the hall simply for walking past her and saying, "Hello." Wendy wants to break the cycle that has developed by avoiding doing anything that Jennifer would view as intrusive. She hopes that she will be able to assure Jennifer that she can be trusted and that Jennifer will be able to lower her defenses and become more open with her.

In the first dialogue, "Getting Acquainted," Wendy begins by trying not to make any direct moves that Jennifer might find objectionable. For example, she does not look at her or address her directly. Wendy tries to let Jennifer feel like she is in control of the situation. For example,

Wendy imitates Jennifer to give her the feeling that Wendy's actions are being controlled by Jennifer. She also backs off immediately when Jennifer shows that she is becoming the least bit defensive. In addition, she tries to get Jennifer to come to her rather than going to Jennifer. She uses an activity that she suspects Jennifer will enjoy as the context for their interaction. These strategies work to make Jennifer more open to Wendy. She comes to accept more direct moves on Wendy's part such as Wendy's handing the pen to her. Also, Jennifer begins to initiate social contact by taking Wendy's hand for drawing and by coming over to sit and stand near Wendy.

In the second dialogue, "Physical Therapy in an Exercise Activity", Joni uses the same strategies to try to develop a positive relationship with Jennifer. Joni's activity is a little more difficult because it is one that Jennifer has always found to be impossible so she is already upset when Joni first sees her. Also, the activity requires that Joni touch and manipulate Jennifer. Joni thinks that Jennifer would find the touching and manipulating more acceptable if Jennifer felt like she were in control of it. Therefore, instead of taking and moving Jennifer's hands, Joni lets Jennifer's hands ride on hers so that Jennifer can pull away at anytime she wants. Also, she allows Jennifer to direct the activity by letting her stop it whenever she wants. As soon as she can, she gets Jennifer to initiate the movement to give Jennifer an even greater sense of control. These strategies put Jennifer at ease and enable her to participate in her physical therapy activity. By the third dialogue, "Events of a Week," much time has passed, and Jennifer and Wendy have developed a relationship that enables both Wendy and Jennifer to be less cautious.

Enhancing Sensitivity

Respond promptly to Jennifer's signals of agitation to help her feel safe and comfortable with adults.
Recognize Jennifer's subtle nonsymbolic behaviors to encourage appropriate, nonaggressive communication expressions and to make it unnecessary for her to be aggressive.
Focus on Jennifer's subtle behaviors that signal a readiness to interact.
Respond sensitively to all of Jennifer's nonsymbolic communications to give her a greater sense of control and to motivate her to communicate more.

Wendy and Joni know that recognizing and responding to Jennifer's attempts at communication are critical to helping Jennifer to feel more in control and relaxed. Being responsive is something of a challenge because Jennifer's nonsymbolic communications are indeed subtle. They have to be sensitive to behaviors such as watching, smiling, showing a relaxed expression, coming over, and rocking slowly, all of which mean that Jennifer is more open to interaction. They have to recognize turning away, pulling away, frowning, showing an agitated expression, whimpering, and rocking fast, all of which mean that she has had enough. At one point, Jennifer uses dropping the pen on the table and placing her hand in a certain position on the table to request that Wendy begin drawing. Jennifer uses a few signals that are easier to recognize and interpret such as pushing Joni's hands up to initiate a stretching motion in physical therapy and pushing a drawing of Joni diving to the floor to catch a balloon to Joni to request that she reenact the dive. In any case, both Wendy and Joni show the extreme sensivity that the situation demands.

Both service providers are careful to use communication that Jennifer can understand. They both use drawing and pointing to communicate with Jennifer. They also use acting things out to communicate. For example, when Joni wants Jennifer to stand up, she stands up herself. When Wendy wants Jennifer to sift the flour into the bowl during cooking, she demonstrates sifting to convey this to Jennifer.

Increasing Opportunities

Enable Jennifer to become an active, social partner by providing opportunities for her to interact.

Provide pauses during familiar events to allow Jennifer an opportunity to direct the behavior of others.

Enable Jennifer to make choices.

Wendy and Joni provide many opportunities to interact. For example, Wendy invites Jennifer to interact by going over to sit by her, by sitting down to entice Jennifer to come over to sit down with her, by offering Jennifer the pen to draw with her, and by offering materials for her to use communicatively during a cooking sequence. Joni offers Jennifer opportunities to interact when she comes in and begins exercising to entice Jennifer to join her, when she knocks over a box that holds audio tapes to get Jennifer to come over to pick them up, when she takes turns with Jennifer putting the tapes away.

Both service providers use pausing in known routines to get Jennifer to participate and communicate. For example, Wendy uses pausing in drawing to signal Jennifer to take a turn drawing, and Joni uses pausing in exercising to get Jennifer to initiate the exercise action. However, Wendy and Jennifer are cautious about when they use pauses. They only use pauses when Jennifer is relaxed because they know that when she is agitated, she responds to a pause as if it where a directive and reacts defensively.

Sequencing Experiences

Organize routines that are clear and consistent within daily events to enhance Jennifer's sense of familiarity and predictability and to give her a sense of order.

Increase Jennifer's participation in social and instructional activities by providing a calendar of forthcoming daily events.

Wendy and Joni know that confusion and surprises make Jennifer feel out of control and cause her to raise her defenses. Therefore, they are careful to organize Jennifer's experiences into predictable routines and to keep her informed of the routine through a calendar. Jennifer's calendar is made up of drawings. Each drawing on the calendar represents an activity that Jennifer does during the day. First thing in the morning, Wendy and Jennifer go to the calendar to look at the first drawing that represents the first activity. Wendy points to the first drawing and uses a communication at Jennifer's level to indicate the activity. For example, if the first activity is grooming, Wendy points to the drawing of Jennifer washing her face, using a washcloth to demonstrate. She hands the washcloth to Jennifer to see if Jennifer will make any gesture with it or communicate about any aspect of the activity. Then, they go to the activity. When the activity is finished, they come back to the calendar. Wendy points to the picture again, makes the washing motion with the washcloth over her face, then makes the finished signal. Again, she hands the cloth to Jennifer. Jennifer has the opportunity to communicate about the activity that is now completed. Then, they go on to the next drawing for the next activity. Since they have been using a predictable routine and the calendar with Jennifer, they have noticed that her behavior has shown marked improvement.

Utilizing Movement

Incorporate movements matched to Jennifer's actions to increase the quality of her nonsymbolic behaviors.

Demonstrate actions with movements to communicate clearly to Jennifer and to expand her
   own repertoire of movements that can be communicative.
Select movements that accommodate Jennifer's ability to interact within particular contexts.
Use movements or communicative behaviors to draw Jennifer's attention to people as communication partners.

Wendy uses movement with Jennifer by letting Jennifer's hand ride on Wendy's to request
that Jennifer participate in drawing with her. Jennifer uses sliding her hand under and moving
Wendy's hand to get Wendy to draw with her. Joni uses moving Jennifer through stretching to
request Jennifer's participation, and to instruct her in the movement she is to do. Jennifer also
uses the pushing of Joni's hands up to initiate the stretching motion.

Both service providers also use demonstrations to communicate with Jennifer. For example, Joni uses rising to standing to request that Jennifer stand, and Wendy uses mimicking actions to describe those actions to Jennifer. Wendy also uses demonstrating sifting to get Jennifer
to sift the flour. Although Wendy offers Jennifer the opportunity to communicate by demonstrating with the sifter, Jennifer does not do it. However, later, when they are communicating
about cutting the cookie dough by reenacting the activity using Play-doh, Jennifer does participate in the reenaction by cutting the doh and putting it on the cookie sheet.

Finally, Wendy, Joni, and Jennifer use drawings of movements to communicate about
those movements. For example, Wendy uses drawings of Jennifer putting a book away to get
her to carry out the action, and Joni uses a drawing of herself diving to the floor to remind
Jennifer of this dive, which Jennifer then uses to request that Joni repeat the dive.

JENNIFER DIALOGUE #1: Getting Acquainted

Wendy is a new teacher. She has heard from other teachers that Jennifer is volatile and aggressive. She is especially belligerent when she is touched, and when the teacher is being directive. Wendy thinks Jennifer is probably just overly defensive. She has decided to take a slow and easy approach to try to assure Jennifer and to enable her to lower her defenses. She begins by observing Jennifer for a while.

GUIDELINES & STRATEGIES	ADULT	LEARNER
		Jennifer walks around the room stopping to look closely and intently at things with patterns. Sometimes she stops for long periods and rocks, shakes her head, and giggles. She smiles the entire time. Finally, she sits down at the table.
♡ Nurturance: Create a positive setting for interactions	Wendy **goes over to the table and sits down. In order to avoid threatening Jennifer, she does not look at her or say anything.**	
		Jennifer immediately **stops rocking and smiling.** She seems to be waiting for something.
		After a few minutes, when Wendy does not do anything, Jennifer goes back to **rocking and smiling,** though she **keeps her eye on Wendy.**
▣▶ Movement: Use movements as communicative behaviors	Wendy begins to **imitate** Jennifer's movements, because she knows this is an effective way of getting the student's attention as well as a good way to break the ice. She **rocks, drums her fingers, picks up a book, examines** it closely, **stands up,** and **rocks** while standing as Jennifer performs these actions. Of	

145

GUIDELINES & STRATEGIES	ADULT	LEARNER
	course, Wendy does not imitate any socially unacceptable behaviors such as eye poking, face slapping, light gazing, or light playing (e.g., moving arms/hands to play with shadows and brightness of light sources) because she does not want to encourage Jennifer's use of stereotypical behaviors.	
		Jennifer **watches** with interest.
Opportunity: Provide opportunities to interact	Wendy thinks things are going well enough, so she goes back to the table, **sits down,** and **waits.**	
		Jennifer **comes over** immediately and **sits down** next to Wendy.
	Wendy thinks she has Jennifer's attention, so she tries to get Jennifer to focus on something she does. She decides to try drawing because Jennifer is so attracted to patterns. Also, she wants to know if Jennifer understands drawings because she could use them to communicate with her if she does.	
Nurturance: Focus on individual's interest	She **takes out** a pen and some paper.	
		Jennifer **watches.**
Sensitivity: Recognize nonsymbolic behaviors	**Wendy quietly says,** "Yes, look," and **nods.**	
		Jennifer **frowns and looks away.**
	Wendy realizes she's overstepped the bounds of Jennifer's tolerance for being intruded upon.	
Movement: Use movement as communicative behavior *Nurturance: Create a positive setting for interactions*	She **begins drawing** and **talking,** but without addressing Jennifer. "I'm drawing Wendy," and **points** to herself. Wendy doesn't really expect Jennifer to understand her words, but she continues to talk because she thinks it might be soothing to Jennifer.	

GUIDELINES & STRATEGIES	ADULT	LEARNER

"I'm drawing Wendy's hair," and **runs her hands through her hair.** "I'm drawing Wendy's face," and **points** to her face. Wendy **draws the nose and the mouth, but no eyes.**

Opportunity: Provide opportunities to interact

She **puts the pen down** and **waits** to give Jennifer a chance to participate without intruding on her.

Jennifer, who has been watching the drawing very closely, **picks up the pen and draws the eyes.**

Sensitivity: Respond contingently

Wendy forgets herself and says enthusiastically, "Yes, eyes!" She **points** to her eyes, and **looks at** Jennifer directly.

Jennifer **turns away quickly** and **begins to whimper.**

Sensitivity: Recognize nonsymbolic behaviors

Wendy **backs off** realizing that Jennifer is becoming defensive.

Sequencing: Establish routines

She goes back to **drawing** and **talking** quietly without really addressing Jennifer.

Movement: Use movements as communicative behaviors

She says, "I'm drawing Wendy sitting in the chair," and **points** to the chair.

She is careful to always use nonsymbolic communications in addition to her language and to model expressions Jennifer could come to use so that Jennifer can better understand her.

Opportunity: Provide opportunities to interact

She **draws all but one leg of the chair, puts the pen down,** and **waits** to give Jennifer an opportunity to participate.

Jennifer **picks up the pen and draws a rough vertical line for the leg.**

Nurturance: Focus on individual's interest

Wendy contains herself. She responds simply by **running her finger down the line** and saying, "Leg," while **pointing** to the leg on the chair.

GUIDELINES & STRATEGIES	ADULT	LEARNER
Movement: Select movements that accommodate the learner's ability to interact	Wendy quietly says, "I'll draw Jennifer." She **points** to Jennifer **without touching** her and **without looking** at her.	
	As she draws, she **names the parts** and **points** to them as she did with the drawing of herself.	
	She **draws all but one arm and the head.**	
Opportunity: Provide opportunity to interact	She **puts down the pen** and **waits.**	
Movement: Use movements as communicative behaviors	Wendy says, "Arm," and **points** to Jennifer's arm.	
		Jennifer picks up the pen and draws a horizontal line for the arm.
	Wendy says, "Head," and **points** to Jennifer's head.	
		Jennifer draws the circle for the head.
	Wendy now knows that Jennifer can draw lines and circles, and she understands that they are not just lines and circles, but drawings of real things. Now, she wants to find out if Jennifer can follow directions given in pictures.	
Opportunity: Create need for requests	She **holds out her hand** to Jennifer to get Jennifer to give her the pen.	
		Jennifer puts the pen in Wendy's hand.
Sensitivity: Respond contingently	Wendy **responds,** "Good. Now, I'll draw the chair," as she **points** to Jennifer's chair.	
		Jennifer is watching attentively. Her face is relaxed.
Opportunity: Utilize time-delay	Wendy **draws all but the legs of the chair, extends the pen to Jennifer,** and **pauses.**	
	She wants to see if Jennifer is relaxed enough to tolerate such a direct move.	
	Wendy **can tell that Jennifer is agitated.**	

GUIDELINES & STRATEGIES	ADULT	LEARNER
		Jennifer's face expresses confusion, but she **takes the pen, quickly draws the legs,** and **drops the pen** on the table.
Sensitivity: Recognize individual's readiness for interaction	Wendy can see that Jennifer is agitated because her face is contorted and she's starting to whimper.	
		Soon Jennifer's face **relaxes.**
	Wendy thinks Jennifer is ready to begin again.	
Movement: Use movements as communicative behaviors	Wendy says as if to herself, "Hmm, what does this picture say? Wendy is sitting . . .," she **points** to herself and the chair, ". . . and Jennifer is . . ." She **points** to Jennifer and Jennifer's chair.	
		Jennifer **looks at the picture,** and **stands next** to her chair as drawn.
	Wendy now knows that Jennifer can follow directions that are given in drawings. This means that Wendy will be able to use drawings to inform Jennifer of upcoming events and to request actions from her. Also, because the drawing activity seems to provide a good context for the two of them to participate in an interaction together, Wendy thinks it will stimulate Jennifer to communicate. With Jennifer's drawing ability, she may even be able to use drawing to convey information herself. But Wendy's concern at the moment is to get on better terms with Jennifer.	
		Jennifer's **arms are resting** on the table and she is **rocking.**
Opportunity: Provide opportunities to interact	Wendy **slides her hand under Jennifer's** and **waits** to see what Jennifer will do.	
		Jennifer starts **rocking faster** but **does not move her hand.**

GUIDELINES & STRATEGIES	ADULT	LEARNER
	Wendy realizes that speed of rocking is a good barometer of how much Jennifer can tolerate. Slow rocking means she is calm and open, and fast rocking means she is agitated and defensive.	
Movement: Select movements that accommodate the learner's ability to interact	When Jennifer relaxes a little, Wendy **picks up the pen with Jennifer's hand on her hand and draws a picture of the book** that is lying on the table.	
Opportunity: Utilize time-delay	She **points** to the book and **pauses** to see what Jennifer will do.	
		Jennifer takes the pen and scribbles over the drawing to represent writing. She drops the pen on the table.
Nurturance: Expand on child-initiated behavior	Wendy says, "Writing," **makes a writing motion** and **points** to the writing on the book.	
Opportunity: Provide opportunities to interact	She **pauses.**	
		Jennifer picks up the pen and drops it on the table.
Opportunity: Utilize time-delay	Wendy realizes that Jennifer wants her to draw, but she wants Jennifer to make a more direct move. Because Jennifer does not seem agitated, Wendy thinks she can afford to **wait** her out for a few seconds without Jennifer becoming too upset.	
		Jennifer puts her hand back on the table where it was when Wendy picked it up before. She is starting to rock faster.
Movement: Use movements as communicative behaviors	Wendy senses that it is time to act and **pushes her hand under Jennifer's hand.**	
Movement: Select movements that accommodate the learner's ability to interact	They **begin to make a drawing** of Jennifer holding the book.	

GUIDELINES & STRATEGIES	ADULT	LEARNER
Sequencing: Establish routines	As before, they take turns, and **Wendy names** and **points** to the parts to be drawn.	
Sequencing: Provide turn-taking opportunities	Then **they begin a drawing** of Jennifer's action of putting the book in the cabinet. When they are almost finished with the figure of Jennifer, Wendy **pauses** to signal Jennifer's turn.	
		Jennifer pushes her hand under Wendy's hand and draws the rest of the figure.
	Wendy is surprised at Jennifer's move for social contact, and realizes that Jennifer might really be quite willing to interact once she feels secure.	
		When they are finished, Jennifer looks at each of the drawings. She picks up the book and puts it away.
		Jennifer returns to the table and sits down.
Opportunity: Provide opportunities to interact	Wendy **slips her hand under Jennifer's hand and says,** "More?"	
		Jennifer shakes Wendy's hand off.
Sensitivity: Recognize nonsymbolic behaviors	Wendy **responds,** "OK, we're finished!"	
		As the day goes on, Jennifer watches Wendy closely. Sometimes she comes over and stands near her, but doesn't look at her.
Sensitivity: Recognize individual's readiness for interaction	Wendy **follows Jennifer's lead** and sometimes goes over and stands near her without making contact.	
		One time, Jennifer comes over and begins rocking.

GUIDELINES & STRATEGIES	ADULT	LEARNER
▶ *Movement: Use movements matched to the level of the learner's actions*	Wendy **mimics Jennifer's rocking.** **Accidentally, they bump into each other.**	
		Jennifer **laughs.**
▣ *Sequencing: Utilize patterns in games*	Wendy **bumps into her** again.	
		Jennifer **laughs.**
▣ *Sequencing: Utilize patterns in games and provide turn-taking opportunities*	Wendy **repeats** the bumping several times and then **pauses.**	
		Jennifer **bumps** into **Wendy** and laughs. They continue the game until Jennifer loses interest and walks away.

Wendy is confident that respecting the limits Jennifer sets will allow Jennifer to be less defensive and more open to Wendy and to instruction. In addition, she thinks that the use of drawing for communicative purposes will help Jennifer to understand, use, and develop more and better communication.

JENNIFER DIALOGUE #2: Physical Therapy Session in an Exercise Activity

In Jennifer's second dialogue, Wendy has arranged for the physical therapy sessions for her students to be incorporated into group exercise activities. She hopes that this will be a better atmosphere for all of her students, but especially to create a positive setting for Joni, the Physical Therapist, and Jennifer to cooperatively exercise. Physical therapy has been a nightmare for Jennifer because of her aversion to being touched. Joni, the Physical Therapist, was frustrated because it was always such a struggle. Wendy, the teacher, had talked to Joni about taking a slow and easy approach and letting Jennifer take the lead. She explained that Jennifer is so difficult because she is so defensive. She is defensive because she feels out of control. If Joni would try letting Jennifer take the lead for a while, her defenses would drop and she would be much easier to work with. All that she needs to do is to respond to Jennifer's signals to stop and to let her signal when she is ready for more. Joni is a little afraid to try it because she thinks Jennifer hates physical therapy, and that if she could stop it, she would. She worries that Jennifer would have to go without therapeutic exercises for a long time while they work on developing a relationship. She is concerned that Jennifer's problem of rounded shoulders and scoliosis might worsen in the interim. Wendy assured her that it would take no time at all.

In the school gym, Wendy is leading an aerobics activity with a small group of students from her room and peers from a regular classroom. Joni will conduct some special therapeutic activities with Jennifer during this time. A paraprofessional and student teacher are also working with some students on special exercises.

GUIDELINES & STRATEGIES	ADULT	LEARNER
Sensitivity: Recognize nonsymbolic behaviors	Joni is doubtful about the new approach, but when she enters the gym and Jennifer starts to **cry and bang her head,** she decides that anything is preferable to spending another session fighting with her.	
Sensitivity: Recognize individual's readiness for interaction	When Joni comes in, she does not go over close to Jennifer, but **waves** and **calls,** "Hi, Jennifer!" She wants Jennifer to come over on her own.	
Nurturance: Create a positive setting for interactions	She tries to lure her over by **putting a tape in the tape machine** and **starting to exercise herself.**	
		Jennifer watches with interest.
Nurturance: Create a positive setting for interactions	Joni does not make a move toward Jennifer. She **continues exercising.**	
		Jennifer begins rocking and gazing at the lights.

GUIDELINES & STRATEGIES	ADULT	LEARNER
♡ *Nurturance: Create a positive setting for interactions*	Joni is losing heart, but she **changes the tape** to try to recapture Jennifer's attention.	
		Jennifer starts watching again.
♡ *Nurturance: Focus on individual's interest*	Joni does not think that Jennifer is going to come over. She has one last plan. She knows that Jennifer likes to pick things up and put them away, so she **knocks over her box of tapes.**	
🚪 *Opportunity: Provide opportunities to interact*	She **waits** to see what Jennifer will do.	
		Jennifer comes right over and starts picking up the tapes.
♡ *Nurturance: Expand on child-initiated behavior*	Joni wants to establish contact, so she **picks up a tape** and puts it in a small open box and **pushes the box toward Jennifer.** Joni is careful not to directly contact Jennifer.	
		A few moments pass. **Jennifer pulls the box toward herself and takes the tape out.**
📑 *Sequencing: Establish routines*	Joni **starts putting tapes in the box,** too, **alternating turns** with Jennifer.	
		Jennifer stays close by when they are finished. Jennifer examines the tape box and the tape recorder, she rocks, and brushes her hair away from her face.
▦ *Movement: Use movements as communicative behaviors*	Joni **sits next to Jennifer** and **copies her movements** for several minutes. This is what Wendy, the teacher, recommended to break the ice. Then Joni **says,** "Let's start."	
		Jennifer begins rocking fast and whimpering.

GUIDELINES & STRATEGIES	ADULT	LEARNER
	Joni thinks that Jennifer is whimpering because she expects Joni to begin to physically manipulate her through the exercises. Instead, Joni does not take her arms, but **slides her hands under Jennifer's hands** and then **lifts their arms** in the usual stretching motion of their arm exercises.	
Movement: Select movements that accommodate the learner's ability to interact		
		Jennifer does not resist at first, but then retracts her arms.
Sensitivity: Recognize nonsymbolic behaviors *Nurturance: Provide support*	Joni **responds,** "Jennifer says, 'Wait,' OK!" Joni **folds her hands to indicate waiting,** and **pauses.**	
Movement: Select movements that accommodate the learner's ability to interact	After about a half minute, Joni **slides her hands under Jennifer's hands** and **they stretch.** This method allows Joni to move Jennifer without Jennifer feeling manipulated.	
		Jennifer doesn't resist for a minute, but then retracts her hands.
Sensitivity: Recognize nonsymbolic behaviors *Nurturance: Provide support* *Sequencing: Establish routines*	Joni **responds,** "Jennifer says, 'Wait.'" She **folds her hands** and **pauses.** Now that they have **repeated the action,** Joni thinks that Jennifer understands the activity well enough so that if Joni pauses Jennifer will be able to initiate the action. **Joni pauses.**	
		Jennifer initiates the action by pushing their arms up.
Sensitivity: Recognize nonsymbolic behaviors	Joni **responds,** "Yes! You do it!" Joni is surprised that not only is Jennifer not resisting her exercises, she is initiating them. Joni realizes that Jennifer did not resist the exercises because she dislikes moving, as Joni originally thought. She resisted them because she cannot tolerate being physically manipulated at all.	

GUIDELINES & STRATEGIES	ADULT	LEARNER
		Jennifer **retracts her hands.**
♡ *Nurturance: Provide support* 🚪 *Opportunity: Provide opportunities to interact*	Joni **responds,** "Yes, let's wait." She **folds her hands.** After the pause, Joni **slips her hands under Jennifer's hands** and **waits.**	
		Jennifer **pushes their hands up in the stretching motion.**
✍ *Sensitivity: Recognize nonsymbolic behaviors*	Joni **responds,** "Yes, you do it!" Joni is really pleased that Jennifer is performing the stretching voluntarily because she knows that Jennifer can better exercise her muscles when she moves herself rather than letting Joni move her.	
		Joni and Jennifer repeat the activity in the same way until Jennifer starts retracting her hands when Joni slips her hands under them.
✍ *Sensitivity: Recognize individual's readiness for interaction*	Joni **responds,** "Finished. Good!" Joni **brings out** an oversized balloon and **sets it on the floor** in front of Jennifer.	
		Jennifer **picks it up, smiling broadly, and pushes it toward Joni.**
✍ *Sensitivity: Respond contingently* 🚪 *Opportunity: Create need for requests*	Joni **responds** by taking it. She **pauses** to see if Jennifer will communicate to her what to do.	
		Jennifer **pushes Joni's hand with the balloon up to her mouth.**
✍ *Sensitivity: Respond contingently*	Joni **responds,** "Blow it up," and **begins blowing.** When she's finished, she **stands up** and **begins batting the balloon** over her head.	
		Jennifer **watches, rocks excitedly, and giggles, but does not get up.**

GUIDELINES & STRATEGIES	ADULT	LEARNER
♡ *Nurturance: Create a positive setting for interactions*	She wants Jennifer to continue to stretch, but she also wants them to have fun together.	
♡ *Nurturance: Create a positive setting for interactions*	Joni could tell Jennifer to get up or she could pull her up, but then Jennifer would get upset and the activity would be finished. Instead, she **sits down across from Jennifer** and **continues the batting game.**	
▤ *Sequencing: Provide turn-taking opportunities*	She **bats the balloon** in Jennifer's direction.	
		Jennifer **begins to try to keep the balloon off the ground** and inadvertently does the stretching Joni wants her to do.
♡ *Nurturance: Expand on child-initiated behavior*	By accident, the balloon goes in Joni's direction. **Joni starts batting it and stands up.**	
		Jennifer **stands up.**
⬉ *Sensitivity: Respond contingently* ▤ *Sequencing: Utilize patterns in games*	Joni **responds,** "Yes, stand up," and nods. She **pushes the balloon to Jennifer,** and says, "Jennifer's turn."	
		Jennifer **bats the balloon.**
♡ *Nurturance: Create a positive setting for interactions*	Joni **becomes animated** because things are going so well. She says, "Don't let it fall," and as she sees it falling she **dives for it.**	
		Jennifer **watches** and **laughs.**
	Joni has seen the new teacher use drawing with Jennifer to capture moments Jennifer may be motivated to communicate about. Joni would like to try it herself.	
⬒ *Opportunity: Provide opportunities to interact*	She **gets out paper and pens** and says, "Let's draw Joni diving for the balloon."	
▶ *Movement: Use movements as communicative behaviors*	She **points** to herself, she **mimes the dive,** and **points** at the balloon.	

GUIDELINES & STRATEGIES	ADULT	LEARNER
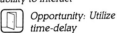 *Movement: Select movements that accommodate the learner's ability to interact* *Opportunity: Utilize time-delay*	She **slips her hand under Jennifer's hand** and **together they draw** the scene, **taking turns.** Joni **draws her head and body and pauses.**	
		Jennifer is watching intently and appears interested in the activity. Jennifer takes the pen and draws the arms and legs.
Opportunity: Provide opportunities to interact	Joni **points** to the balloon and **extends** the pen to Jennifer.	
		Jennifer draws a circle for the balloon.
Nurturance: Expand on child-initiated behavior	Joni **names** and **points** to or **pantomimes each thing as they draw it.** Wendy has told Joni how important it is to use nonsymbolic expressions with Jennifer if she wants to be understood, because Jennifer doesn't understand much language, but she does understand pointing and pantomime.	
Movement: Use movements as communicative behaviors	When they are finished with the drawing, Joni **points** to the picture and **reenacts the dive.**	
		Jennifer laughs and pushes the picture to Joni.
Sensitivity: Respond contingently	Joni **responds,** "Jennifer says, "do it again!" and she **dives for the floor.**	
		Jennifer pushes the picture toward Joni several more times and Joni **responds** by performing.
Sequencing: Establish routines	Joni **signals finished by saying,** "Finished" **and putting the picture and pen in a container.**	
		Jennifer is watching.
Movement: Use movements as communicative behaviors	Joni **stands up and looks at Jennifer.**	

GUIDELINES & STRATEGIES	ADULT	LEARNER
		Jennifer stands up.
▯ *Opportunity: Provide opportunities to interact*	Joni **extends the container toward Jennifer.**	
		Jennifer **puts a couple fingers** lightly under the ridge.
♡ *Nurturance: Provide support*	Joni **releases some of her hold** so Jennifer carries some of the weight and **walks** with Jennifer to put the container away.	
		When they reach the shelf, **Jennifer pauses.**
✐ *Sensitivity: Recognize nonsymbolic behaviors*	Joni **says,** "I put it," as she points to herself and **makes a gesture** of pushing the container on the shelf.	
		Jennifer **makes eye contact.**
▮▶ *Movement: Use movements as communicative behaviors*	Joni puts the container away. She **gestures,** tossing a ball, as she refers to the basketball game the group of students are playing, **points** to the group, and **pauses.**	
		Jennifer **looks at the group.**
▮▶ *Movement: Use movements as communicative behaviors*	Joni **begins walking** over to the group.	
		Jennifer **follows.**
	They join in the game playing side-by-side.	
	When it comes time for Joni to leave, Jennifer follows her to the door. Joni can hardly believe this is the same student who used to cry and fight during physical therapy. She had thought that Jennifer hated her and physical therapy, but now she knows that Jennifer just couldn't tolerate the way they used to do it.	

JENNIFER DIALOGUE #3: Cooking Events during One Week

Jennifer and another student, Doug, are getting ready to go to the grocery story to buy the ingredients to make cookies. They are standing with Wendy, their teacher, in front of the cabinet where the food is kept. They are going to check their supplies.

GUIDELINES & STRATEGIES	ADULT	LEARNER
	<u>Monday</u>	
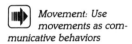 Movement: Use movements as communicative behaviors	Wendy has a stack of drawings of the ingredients for the cookies. She **takes the drawing of the sugar.** She **makes a show of looking at the drawing, searching through the cabinet, and looking at the drawing** to communicate to Jennifer and Doug what she wants them to do.	
		Doug and Jennifer are watching.
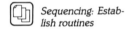 Sequencing: Establish routines	Wendy **makes a show of finding the sugar, matching it to the drawing, and putting the picture face down on the cabinet.**	
	She **gives the drawing of the flour to Jennifer and points** from the drawing to the cabinet to get Jennifer to look in the cabinet for the flour.	
		Jennifer is always very active and attentive in activities with drawings and matching. **She smiles broadly as she searches through the cabinet for the flour. When she finds the flour she giggles** and spends a long time **comparing the bag of flour to the drawing.**
Nurturance: Create a positive setting for interactions	Wendy **claps** and says, "Very good!"	
Sensitivity: Recognize individual's readiness for interaction	She wants Jennifer to finish up, but she wants to avoid doing it through making a command because Jennifer is so hyper-defensive to directives. Instead, Wendy **hands Doug the drawing of the brown sugar.**	

GUIDELINES & STRATEGIES	ADULT	LEARNER
		Jennifer notices Wendy giving the drawing to Doug. She puts the drawing of the flour face **down** on top of the sugar drawing and steps aside.
		Doug begins looking for the brown sugar.

♡ *Nurturance: Focus on individual's interest*

Wendy **describes what Doug is doing by copying his actions and saying,** "Doug is looking."

Although Wendy is directing her communication to Doug, she wants to convey information to both Doug and Jennifer. She knows that Jennifer couldn't tolerate Wendy's standing close to her and describing her actions this way; however, Jennifer does attend when Wendy does this with Doug. Therefore, Wendy uses nonsymbolic description of Doug's actions to teach Doug and Jennifer to understand more nonsymbolic communication.

👐 *Sensitivity: Respond to individual's level of communication*

In addition, she **pairs her words with Doug's actions** to help them understand more language.

Doug finds the brown sugar. Wendy **points to the brown sugar** and says, "There it is." She **pats Doug** on the back.

♡ *Nurturance: Provide affection*

Doug smiles. He puts the picture of the brown sugar face down on the stack of drawings they have used.

♡ *Nurturance: Expand on child-initiated behavior*

♡ *Nurturance: Provide affection*

As Doug puts the drawing on the stack, Wendy **describes what he does by copying his actions and saying,** "Put the drawing away. Very good!" She **tousles his hair.**

   Sometimes Doug acts as if he is walking in his sleep. Wendy has found that if she tousles and jostles him from time-to-time, it keeps him going for his activities.

   In addition, Jennifer always smiles and

GUIDELINES & STRATEGIES	ADULT	LEARNER

GUIDELINES & STRATEGIES

ADULT

giggles when Wendy lavishes encouragement on Doug. It is as if Jennifer receives some encouragement from seeing Doug responded to in this way.

LEARNER

Doug smiles. Jennifer smiles and giggles.

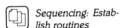 *Sequencing: Establish routines*

Wendy **takes another drawing from the stack** of drawings of the ingredients for the cookies. She **gets the drawing of the vanilla.**

She deliberately took the vanilla because she knows they do not have it and she wants to model for the students what to do if the item is not in the cabinet.

Movement: Use movements as communicative behaviors

Sequencing: Establish routines

She **makes a show of looking for the vanilla.** When she does not find it, she **points to the drawing, shakes her head, and puts it face up on the counter.**

Jennifer and Doug are watching.

Wendy **gives Jennifer the drawing of the baking soda.**

Jennifer searches through the cabinet. When she does not find the baking soda, she puts the drawing of the soda face up on the counter, on top of the drawing of the vanilla.

When they are finished going through this process of looking for the ingredients as pictured on the cards, they have a stack of drawings of items they do not need at the store and a stack of items they do need. They take the drawings of the items they need to get at the store as a grocery list.

Tuesday

Sequencing: Establish routines

Wendy **uses the stack of drawings of ingredients to get Jennifer and Doug to collect the ingredients to make the cookies.**

GUIDELINES & STRATEGIES	ADULT	LEARNER
	She has added drawings of other things they will need including measuring cups and spoons, an egg beater, and a mixing bowl.	
	Once all the materials are collected, Wendy presents Jennifer and Doug with a recipe conveyed through drawings. There is one drawing for each step in the process of making the dough. The drawings are collated to make a book.	
Sequencing: Establish routines	Wendy **shows them the first page that depicts sifting the flour.**	
Movement: Select movements that accommodate the learner's ability to interact	She **gets the sifter** and **demonstrates scooping the flour and sifting into the measuring cup.**	
Opportunity: Provide opportunities to interact	She **hands the sifter to Jennifer.**	
		Jennifer takes the sifter and **imitates Wendy's sifting action.**
Movement: Use movements as communicative behaviors	Wendy **turns to Doug, points to Jennifer, mimics her sifting action, and says,** "Look Doug, Jennifer is sifting." Again, Wendy directs communication meant for Jennifer to Doug in hopes that Jennifer will take it in.	
Opportunity: Provide opportunities to interact	When Jennifer is finished, Wendy **picks up the flour** and **tips it over the bowl.** She says, "Pour." She **sets the cup down** in front of Jennifer.	
		Jennifer pours the flour into the bowl.
Movement: Use movements as communicative behaviors	Wendy **turns to Doug, points to Jennifer, mimics her pouring action,** and **says,** "Pour." She **says,** "Very good!"	
Sequencing: Establish routines	She **turns the page of the book to reveal a drawing of adding the baking soda.**	
Movement: Use movements as communicative behaviors	She **says,** "Doug," and **demonstrates scooping out the baking soda and pouring it into the bowl.**	

GUIDELINES & STRATEGIES	ADULT	LEARNER
Opportunity: Utilize time-delay	She **holds on to the measuring spoons and the soda** and **waits** to see what Doug will do.	
		Doug reaches toward the soda, looks at Wendy, and vocalizes.
Sensitivity: Recognize nonsymbolic behaviors	**Wendy says,** "Yes! It is Doug's turn," and **passes the spoons and soda to him.**	
		Doug adds the soda to the bowl.
Nurturance: Provide support	Wendy **says,** "Good job!" **and pats him.**	
Sequencing: Establish routines	**The activity continues in the same way until the cookie dough is made.**	
	After they have wrapped it and put it into the refrigerator, they come back to the table to converse about the activity. They use the recipe book and the objects from the activity in their conversation.	
Movement: Use movements as communicative behaviors	Wendy **opens the book to the first page, points to Jennifer, pretends to scoop flour out of the bag with the sifter, pretends to sift into the measuring cup while saying,** "Jennifer sifted," and **pretends to pour into the bowl while saying,** "Jennifer poured."	
Opportunity: Provide opportunities to interact	She **pushes the flour, the sifter, the measuring cup, and the bowl to Jennifer to see if she will use the objects to communicate about sifting.**	
		Jennifer squeezes the sifter.
Movement: Use movements matched to the level of the learner's actions	Wendy **points to Jennifer, mimics sifting, and says** to Doug, "Jennifer sifted."	
Movement: Use movements matched to the level of the learner's actions	Wendy **turns the page.** She **points to Doug, pretends to scoop out the baking soda with the measuring spoons, and pretends to pour it into the bowl, saying,** "Doug put in the soda."	
		Doug takes the spoons and turns them over above the bowl.

GUIDELINES & STRATEGIES	ADULT	LEARNER
Sensitivity: Respond contingently	Wendy **mimics his action** and **says,** "Yes! Doug put the soda in."	
Movement: Use movements as communicative behaviors	Wendy **turns the page in the book.** She **points to the drawing of putting the salt in.**	
Opportunity: Provide opportunities to interact	She **waits to see if any one will do anything.**	
Sensitivity: Recognize nonsymbolic behaviors	Wendy **points to Jennifer and says,** "Yes, Jennifer put in the salt."	
		Doug pushes the spoons to Jennifer.
	Wendy does not want Jennifer to open the salt, but she knows if she tries to stop her now, Jennifer might react in an aggressive way. It is a delicate situation.	
		Jennifer takes the salt and begins to open it.
Sensitivity: Recognize individual's readiness for interaction	Wendy **begins walking her fingers over the table toward the salt to give Jennifer advance warning and time to prepare for Wendy to do something.** Wendy **says,** "Here I come to get the salt." She **watches Jennifer closely** to make sure she is not becoming agitated.	
		Jennifer watches Wendy.
Sensitivity: Recognize nonsymbolic behaviors	Wendy **grabs the salt and holds it until she is sure Jennifer will accept her taking it.**	
		Jennifer lets go of the salt.
Nurturance: Create a positive setting for interactions	Wendy **takes it** and **makes a show of closing the salt.** She **points to Jennifer, pretends to pour the salt into the spoon, and pretends to dump it into the bowl saying,** "Jennifer put in the salt."	
Movement: Use movements matched to the level of the learner's actions	She **waits** to see if Jennifer will do anything.	
Opportunity: Provide opportunities to interact		
		Jennifer does not do anything.

GUIDELINES & STRATEGIES	ADULT	LEARNER

Wendy does not press. She goes onto the next picture. Sometimes when the students are very attentive, they can go through each page in a book and converse about it. Some days, they just cannot attend to more than a couple of pages. Wendy **adjusts to what the students are able to do on any particular day.**

Nurturance: Create a positive setting for interactions

They continue communicating about making the cookie dough in the same way until they have communicated about the whole recipe and process.

Wednesday

Today Doug and Jennifer bake the cookies. After baking Wendy wants to continue to communicate with Doug and Jennifer about the activity. They **converse about the activity by acting it out, using Play-doh to represent the cookie dough and the objects from the activity in their recreation of the baking.**

Movement: Use movements as communicative behaviors

Sequencing: Establish routines

Wendy **indicates the Play-doh and says,** "Cookie dough."

Movement: Use movements matched to the level of the learner's actions

She **looks at Doug and Jennifer and says,** "We cut the dough," while **making a sawing motion with her hand over the dough.** She **holds up a spoon and a knife** and **says,** "Knife or spoon?"

Opportunity: Provide choices

Doug **reaches for the knife.**

Sensitivity: Recognize nonsymbolic behaviors

Wendy **nods and says,** "Yes, we cut with the knife," while **making the sawing motion with her hand.**

Opportunity: Create need for requests

Wendy **looks at Doug and says,** "What did we do?"

Doug **begins cutting pieces off of the Play-doh and putting them on the cookie sheet.**

Sensitivity: Respond contingently

Movement: Use movements as communicative behaviors

Wendy **nods and mimics Doug's actions while saying,** "Yes, we put the cookies on the cookie sheet." Wendy **points to Jennifer and says,** "Jennifer's turn."

GUIDELINES & STRATEGIES	ADULT	LEARNER
		Doug hands Jennifer the knife.
		Jennifer begins to cut the dough and put it on the cookie sheet.
♡ *Nurturance: Provide support*	Wendy **says,** "That's right!"	
	<u>Thursday</u>	
	Jennifer and Doug sell the cookies in the teacher's lounge.	
	At the end of the day, Wendy, Jennifer, and Doug gather at the table where they usually draw in the classroom. Wendy has the plate that held the cookies, a few cookies, the price sign and some money. Wendy **says,** "Draw selling cookies." She **hands some money to Doug and takes a cookie off the plate** to remind Doug and Jennifer of the activity. Then she **points to the paper.** She **says,** "Draw the plate," **points to the plate and puts the pen down near Jennifer.**	
▦▶ *Movement: Use movements as communicative behaviors*		
▯ *Opportunity: Provide opportunities to interact*		
		Jennifer takes the pen and draws a circle for the plate.
♡ *Nurturance: Provide support*	Wendy **says,** "Very good," **and nods and smiles.**	
▤ *Sequencing: Provide turn-taking opportunities*	She **points to the cookies and says,** "Draw cookies." She **gives the pen to Doug.**	
		Doug makes marks resembling cookies on the plate.
✑ *Sensitivity: Recognize nonsymbolic behaviors*	Wendy **says,** "Yes, cookies," **and points to the real cookies** and the cookies in the drawing.	
▦▶ *Movement: Use movements as communicative behaviors*	She **takes the pen.** She **says,** "Draw Jennifer," while **pretending to draw and then pointing to Jennifer.** She **draws all but the arms.** She **puts the pen down.**	
▯ *Opportunity: Provide opportunities to interact*		
		Jennifer takes the pen and draws the arms.

GUIDELINES & STRATEGIES	ADULT	LEARNER
	They go on to draw Doug and one of the teachers who came to buy cookies. When they are finished, Wendy **points to the drawing of the plate.** She **makes a quizzical face and says,** "What?"	
 *Opportunity: Provide opportunities to interact*		
		Doug **points to the plate.**
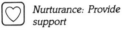 *Nurturance: Provide support* *Sequencing: Provide turn-taking opportunities*	Wendy **says,** "Yes. Very good!" She **points to the drawings of the cookies and looks at Jennifer.**	
		Jennifer doesn't move.
Movement: Use movements as communicative behaviors *Sequencing: Provide turn-taking opportunities*	Wendy **picks up a cookie and a quarter.** She **points to the drawing of the cookies.** She **touches the cookie to the picture and, then, the quarter.** She **sets the cookies and the quarter in front of Jennifer.**	
		Jennifer **picks up the cookies and touches it to the drawing.**
Sensitivity: Respond contingently	Wendy **says,** "Yes, cookies!" They continue communicating about the drawing for some time. Wendy always arranges her activities so that there are plenty of opportunities for her to communicate with the students and for the students to communicate with her.	

Friday

Jennifer and Doug use the money from the sale of the cookies to go the roller rink to skate and have lunch.

Description of Ed and Purposes for His Communication Intervention

Ed, is a 10 year old with severe mental retardation and a mild form of cerebral palsy. He has limited use of his left arm and uses his left leg minimally. Sometimes he exhibits restricted coordination, especially while walking or running. Ed can independently perform all of the skills necessary to manage his personal hygiene. When assisted by an adult, he can carry out many home care and work activities.

He is beginning to understand some words when they are used systematically within his routine. He understands and uses pointing, pantomime, and other gestures for communication. In addition, he can understand and use drawings for communicative purposes.

Ed's dialogues occur as he serves snacks (#1), takes part in physical education (#2), and participates in community training (#3).

PURPOSES FOR ED'S COMMUNICATION INTERVENTION

Developing Nurturance

Maintain a positive relationship between Ed and his service providers to promote an atmosphere that encourages interactions.

Expand on behaviors initiated by Ed, thereby utilizing and enlarging his communication repertoire.

Use activities that Ed is interested in to motivate him to interact and develop his skills.

In the following dialgoues, Ed's teacher, Sue, and his physical education instructor, Kate, use an affectionate tone of voice and encouraging pats on the back to convey their support of Ed.

Ed's service providers strive to make the activities enjoyable to enable Ed to be relaxed and more open and receptive to interaction. One way they do this is by using activities that Ed is known to enjoy. For example, Sue uses preparing snacks and going to a fast food restaurant as the contexts for their interactions because she knows that these are Ed's special favorites. Kate uses an obstacle course to stimulate communication as well as to help Ed to meet the physical skills she has for him. During the activity, Kate gives Ed a turn to design a course and uses his course as the content for their communicative exchanges.

Both service providers avoid being overly directive and intrusive to create the proper atmosphere for communication to be fostered. Wherever they can, they use Ed's focus of attention as the topic of their interaction. In this way, they are assured of Ed's interest and they avoid having to interrupt Ed or redirect him. One strategy that they use to take advantage of Ed's focus of attention is to watch for what he is looking at and when appropriate, comment on it. For example, Sue notices that Ed is paying attention to the bottle of dishwashing liquid. She brings the bottle closer and says, "Look Ed." She pantomimes squirting soap into the sink and turning on the water. In the gym, Kate notices that Ed is looking at the trampoline. She says, "There's the trampoline," points to it, and makes a jumping motion with her body. During the snack activity, Sue noticed that the spilling of the drink grabbed everybody's attention. She takes this opportunity to describe the incident for the students. Later, Sue selects the spilling of the juice as the topic of conversation after snack because she knows that it is one that everyone is interested in.

Both service providers assume that what Ed is doing at the moment is what has his attention, so often they use his current actions as the topic for communicative exchanges. For example, when Ed is paying attention to setting the table, Sue focuses her communication around the actions he is performing. When Ed is drawing the ladder during the obstacle course activity, Kate says, "Ed is drawing the ladder." She makes the drawing motion, and points to the ladder. When Ed is pulling the bench out of the way as he arranges the obstacle course, Kate says, "Look at Ed pull!", as she makes a pulling motion. Sue also tries to predict what Ed is thinking about and uses that to communicate with him. For example, Sue knows that Ed is thinking about getting the cups so she steps in front of him and says, "Ed is getting the cups." She points to Ed, makes a getting motion, and a drinking motion. When Sue knows that Ed is thinking about whom to pick first to serve juice to, she says, "Who's first?" while making an empty hands gesture, and pointing around the table. When Ed is drawing a picture of himself going through the tunnel, Kate focuses her communication around what Ed is thinking about. She says, "Ed went through the tunnel," points to Ed, and makes the "going through" motion.

Sue and Kate know that when Ed communicates, his attention is focused on his communication, so they often use his communication as the topic for their response. For example, when Ed tells Sue to take the dishes out of the cabinet, Sue says, "Sue take the dishes out of the cabinet," and makes a gesture for Sue and for taking out. When Ed communicates to Sue to take the cups, Sue says, "Carry the cups." She points to herself, makes the carrying motion, and makes a drinking motion. Later, when Ed makes a pouring motion, and looks at Sue, Sue responds by saying, "Oh, Ed needs help," and by making the Sue gesture and the pouring motion.

Both service providers expand on behaviors initiated by Ed to enlarge Ed's communicative repertoire. For example, at the fast food restaurant, Ed goes to get a napkin and a straw to use while he eats. Sue responds by saying, "You got napkins," and makes a face-wiping motion. On several occasions Ed communicates by pulling the teachers' hands or arms. The adults take the opportunity to model the expression they would rather have him use under the circumstances. For example, when Ed pulls Joni out of her chair, she says, "Ed says, 'Stand up,'" and makes a standing-up motion with her hands and body. Later, when Ed pushes her hand to the paper to request that she draw, Joni expands by saying, "Draw?" and makes the drawing motion.

Enhancing Sensitivity

Recognize Ed's nonsymbolic behaviors as meaningful communication and respond appropriately.

Respond to Ed's behaviors in a manner that is appropriate and relevant to Ed at his level of communication.

Be aware of his readiness or nonreadiness for interaction.

Throughout Ed's dialogues, all of the service providers try to recognize Ed's nonsymbolic behaviors. Ed uses pointing, pulling, pushing, and leading people, vocalizing, drawing, and gesturing to communicate. Each service provider carefully interprets and responds to each communication Ed produces.

Each of the service providers is also careful to use communication with Ed that he can understand. They know that he does not understand much spoken language yet. Signs have been used with him in the past, but he never seemed to understand them any better than he understood spoken language, and he never used them unless he was prompted. Instead, he used pointing and pantomime to communicate. His service providers finally decided that he might understand them better if they also used pointing and pantomime. Of course, they still use spoken language with him, and they do make an effort to try to get him to learn to understand more language, but if they want to get a message across to him, they use pointing, drawing, and pantomime.

Ed is usually attentive and ready for interaction. There are a few occasions when his service providers have to deal with the problem of his not being ready. The few times he had begun to stare off or to self-stimulate disruptively, they are able to regain his attention easily. For example, Sue gets his attention back to the table setting activity by patting the cabinet. Kate gets his attention back to the obstacle course by waving her arms and moving through it in a more animated way. Phil, the paraprofessional, is able to get Ed to stop self-stimulating by putting his arm around him to prevent him from rocking.

Increasing Opportunities

Increase Ed's opportunity to communicate by providing appropriate pauses (e.g., time-delays) during interactions thereby precipitating communicative attempts from him.
Delay assistance or remove materials to encourage further initiations from Ed.
Provide opportunities for Ed to make choices and decisions.

Sue uses pausing in interactions to give Ed an opportunity to communicate with her. For example, after Ed distributes the cups he has on the table, Sue pauses before she begins distributing her cups. This gives Ed a chance to communicate with her about it. Ed responds by pulling Sue to the table and pointing. Sue responds by picking up a cup and pausing to see if Ed will communicate further. He responds by pointing to the table and making a putting motion. Later, when they are drawing about Callie, a classmate, spilling her drink during the snack activity, Sue puts the chalk to the blackboard and pauses to see if anyone will tell her what to draw. Ed responds by pointing to Callie.

Kate also uses pauses to stimulate Ed to communicate. For example, she pauses in pushing her chair to the obstacle course. Ed responds by looking at Kate and pointing to the course. Kate responds by pushing her chair and pausing again. Ed responds by making a pushing motion and pointing to the course. Once Ed has learned the sequence of the obstacle course, Kate pauses before she begins so that Ed can tell her what to do.

During the interaction at the fast food restaurant, Sue pauses before cleaning up a mess to encourage Ed to participate with her. Ed responds by beginning to wipe up. Phil, the paraprofessional who is helping out with community training, pauses to get Ed to tell him where to put his lunch tray. Ed responds by pointing to the table where he wants to sit.

Ed's service providers try to present other situations in which Ed will be stimulated to communicate. For example, Sue knows that Ed will need help pouring the juice during snack, but instead of rushing to help him, she waits for him to communicate a need for assistance. At the restaurant, Ed is given the opportunity to communicate his need to have his tray carried to the table for him. He responds to the opportunity by going to Phil, pulling him up, pointing to his tray, and making a carrying motion.

Ed is offered opportunities to communicate when his service providers give him a choice between alternatives. For example, Sue provides the students choices when she indicates that they are going to draw the spilling of the juice during snack and waits for the students to choose what to draw first. Kate offers Ed choices when it is his turn to set up the obstacle course. For example, she says, "Ball or tube," as she points to the big ball and the cardboard tube. He responds by pushing the ball away and turning the tube up on its end, thus conveying his choice of the tube. Phil offers the students a choice of games when they go to the video games room. The students respond by going to the game they want.

Sequencing Experiences

Establish routines in the daily activities that are clear and consistent and will involve Ed more fully.

Incorporate familiar patterns in games and routines that encourage Ed's participation and communication with others.

Provide opportunities for turn-taking to develop interactions, enabling Ed to experience more of the reciprocal nature of communication.

Use a calendar of drawings with Ed to keep him informed of his activities and to serve as a context for him to communicate with his service providers.

In Ed's dialogues, all of the service providers use routines. The snack activity is a routine with which Ed is familiar. His familiarity allows him to be somewhat independent in his use of communication and in carrying out the activity. When he sees his picture, he goes and touches his teacher's arm to tell her that he is ready to begin. Later, Ed is able to communicate to Sue about putting the cups out on the table because of his knowledge of the table setting routine. In addition, Sue uses Ed's familiarity with the activity to try to teach him to understand more communication. For example, while Ed is independently setting the table, Sue communicates with him by putting his actions into words and motions. Later, when Sue knows that Ed is thinking about getting the cups from the cabinet, she puts his thoughts into communications. She says, "Ed is getting the cups," points to Ed, makes a getting motion, and a drinking motion.

Kate also uses routine with Ed to encourage his use of communication. The gym activity is organized into a sequence of obstacle course, drawing, obstacle course, drawing. Ed knows the routine and so is able to initiate drawing by making a drawing motion after the obstacle course. The obstacle course itself is a sequence that Ed and Kate repeat until Ed knows it. Then, as Kate goes through the course, she pauses as she meets each obstacle and Ed is able to communicate to her what to do. Later, when they are drawing a series of pictures about the obstacle course, Ed calls upon his knowledge of the sequence to communicate to Kate what to draw on each page.

Ed's daily routine is communicated to him through the use of a calendar. Ed's calendar is a sequence of drawings. Each drawing is a depiction of one of the activities that he does during the day. For example, grooming is depicted by a drawing of Ed standing by the mirror, gym is depicted by a drawing of the climbing gym, and lunch is depicted by a drawing of food on a plate. Ed can check the calendar to find out what he is going to do during the day. Also, his teacher can use the calendar as a context to communicate with Ed about his activities. For example, after the snack activity illustrated in Dialogue #1, Sue could go back to the calendar with Ed, point to the picture, and give an empty hands gesture to ask him what happened during snack. Or, she could start to pantomime about the spilling of the juice and give Ed a chance to expand. Or, she could engage him in making a drawing of the actions and communicating about setting the table.

Utilizing Movement

Select movements that accommodate Ed's ability to respond and interact.

Use movements that match Ed's level of communication to increase the quality and quantity of Ed's nonsymbolic behaviors.

Utilize movement activities to encourage greater use of his left arm and leg.

Implement playful physical interactions that Ed enjoys.

Demonstrate actions to incorporate movements as communicative behaviors with Ed.

Ed's service providers are using pantomime to communicate with him. When Ed first started in the program, they wanted to communicate with him about certain actions, one of which was washing hands. At first, they had to actually manipulate him through the action for him to understand. If he wanted to communicate a desire to rub his hands together, he did so by manipulating the teacher's hand to rub his hands together. As he progressed, his service providers were able to communicate with him about an action by moving with him simultaneously. For example, if the teacher wanted to tell him to rub his hands together she would begin to rub her hands together during the washing activity, and pause to give him a chance to join her. He could communicate a desire to rub his hands together by beginning the action, and his teacher could respond by joining him. As he developed, his teachers could communicate with him by demonstrating an action. For example, if the service providers wanted him to wash, they would demonstrate hand washing by actually washing their hands. When they finished the demonstration, he understood what they wanted and could respond by washing himself. Finally, the day came that when they wanted him to wash his hands, they would simply pretend to wash and he could understand the request. Then he could communicate a desire to wash by making a washing motion himself. At this point, it is easy for Ed to understand and to construct gestures to use for communicative purposes because the gestures that are used look like the things they refer to. For example, the eating motion is easy for him to use and understand because it looks like the actual eating action. So far he has not been able to learn to use or understand communications that do not resemble the things they represent such as the signs from sign language for the deaf or the symbols used in spoken language. His service providers try to give him the opportunity to learn to understand and use language, but they know that if they really want to get a message across to Ed, they must supplement any spoken language with nonsymbolic forms of expression.

ED DIALOGUE #1: Serving Snack

The bell rings at the end of the last activity, informing the students that the activity is finished and it is time to get ready for snack. All the students know to go over to the refrigerator and see if their picture is posted on the door. This tells them if it is their turn to help. Sue, the teacher, is standing nearby.

GUIDELINES & STRATEGIES	ADULT	LEARNER
		Ed sees his picture and **vocalizes** to the other students. He **goes** over to Sue, the teacher, and **touches** her arm to tell her that he is ready to help.
Opportunity: Utilize time-delay	**Sue responds,** "Good, Ed. What next?" She **pauses,** giving Ed an opportunity to respond.	
		Ed answers her by **gesturing** toward the kitchen area and **pulling her hand** in that direction.
	Together they walk over to where the snack is prepared.	
Movement: Use movements as communicative behaviors	Sue **says,** "Open the cabinet and take out a plate," while making an **opening motion (pantomimes opening the cabinet)** near the cabinet door, a **taking out motion (pantomimes taking out a plate),** and **pointing** to the plate.	
	Sue know that Ed does not understand it when she says, "Open the cabinet," but he does know that when she pantomimes opening the cabinet it means "Open the cabinet." Sue uses the pantomime of opening the cabinet to communicate with Ed about this action and now he can use it when he wants to communicate with her. Sue and Ed use pantomime to communicate about everything they do during the day including setting the table, washing the dishes, washing face and hands, combing hair, and getting, carrying, and putting things down.	

GUIDELINES & STRATEGIES	ADULT	LEARNER
	It was not too long ago that when Sue wanted to communicate about an action like opening the cabinet and taking out a plate, she had to actually open the cabinet and take out a plate. Ed would respond by imitating. Now she uses pantomime and he understands.	
		Ed stops and begins gazing off.
Sequencing: Encourage participation	Sue tries to get his attention in an unintrusive way. She **pats the cabinet and says,** "Look, Ed."	
		Ed looks.
Sequencing: Encourage participation	Sue then holds her **palms up** to **make an empty hands gesture, and says,** "What?"	
		Ed reaches for Sue's hand.
Opportunity: Create need for requests	Sue anticipates that Ed will try to take her hand. She **moves her hands** discreetly out of Ed's reach to see if he can communicate what he wants in a more sophisticated way. **She repeats,** "What?" while making an **empty hands gesture.**	
		Ed makes a taking out gesture, and takes Sue's hand and pushes it toward the cabinet.
Nurturance: Expand on child-initiated behavior	Sue **says,** "Sue take out the dishes," while making a **pigtail gesture** with her hands (Ed's way of referring to Sue by holding both of his fists at either side of his head, as if holding hair in two pigtails), and a **taking out motion.**	
Movement: Use movements as communicative behaviors		
Movement: Select movements that accommodate the learner's ability to respond	"Let's take out," while **pointing** to herself and Ed, making a **taking out motion,** and **bringing his arm** up to the dishes.	
		Ed and Sue take the dishes out. Ed **notices the new bottle** of dishwashing soap by the sink.
Nurturance: Focus on individual's interest	**Sue responds by bringing the bottle toward him** and saying, "Look, Ed."	

GUIDELINES & STRATEGIES	ADULT	LEARNER
		Ed takes it and looks at it.
Movement: Use movements matched to the level of the learner's actions	Sue **pantomimes squirting the soap into the sink and turning on the water.**	
		Ed **smiles and puts the soap back** where it belongs.
Sequencing: Establish routines	Sue **returns to the snack sequence.**	
Movement: Use movements matched to the level of the learner's actions	She helps Ed to hold the stack of dishes in his arms. **She says,** "That's right, Ed carries the dishes to the table." As she speaks, Sue **points** to Ed, makes a **carrying motion,** and **points** to the table.	
		Ed **goes to the table** and **puts one plate** at each student's place.
	Sue always uses nonsymbolic expressions with Ed to help him learn to understand her language, to get her message across, and to model forms of expressions that Ed can learn to use to communicate.	
Movement: Use movements as communicative behaviors	Sue follows him, and describes what Ed is doing in simple terms with gestures. She is careful to communicae with Ed not only when she wants him to do something, but also to comment on what he does and on what he is interested in. **Sue says,** "Ed puts the dishes on the table," while **pointing** to Ed, making a **putting motion,** and **pointing** to the table.	
Movement: Use movements as communicative behaviors	**Sue says,** "Ed picks up a plate," while **pointing** to Ed, making a **picking up motion,** and **pointing** to the plate.	
Nurturance: Provide affection	When Ed is finished, **Sue says,** "Finished with the plates," and makes the **finished sign.** Sue **smiles and pats** Ed on the back.	
		Ed is familiar with the table setting routine so he knows that the next step is to get the cups.

GUIDELINES & STRATEGIES	ADULT	LEARNER
Sensitivity: Respond to individual's level of communication	Sue knows that when Ed starts back toward the cabinet he's thinking about getting the cups. She moves ahead of him so he can see her, **and says,** "Ed is getting the cups." She **points** to Ed, makes a **getting motion,** and makes a **drinking motion.**	
		Ed **gets the cups** out of the cabinet. He pushes them toward Sue.
Sensitivity: Respond contingently *Movement: Respond to movements as communicative behaviors*	Sue **responds,** "Sue carry the cups." She **points** to herself, makes a **carrying motion** and a **drinking motion.**	
Opportunity: Provide opportunities to interact	She **pushes** some back toward Ed so that they can share the work. **She says,** "Ed carry too." She **points** to Ed and makes a **carrying motion.**	
		Ed and Sue **carry the** cups to the table. Ed **distributes** his cups.
Opportunity: Utilize time-delay	When Ed is finished, Sue **pauses** to give Ed an opportunity to direct her to distribute her cups.	
		Ed **pulls Sue** to the table and **points.**
Opportunity: Utilize time-delay	Sue **responds** by **picking up** a cup. She **pauses** briefly to see what Ed will do.	
		Ed **points** to the table and makes a **putting motion.**
Movement: Respond to movement as communicative behaviors	Sue **responds** by **putting** the cup on the table.	
Opportunity: Utilize time-delay	She **pauses** briefly to see what Ed will do.	
		Ed continues to direct Sue to put out the cups using **pointing** and the **putting motion.**
	The other children start to sit down at the table so Ed knows it's time for him to help them get their popcorn and juice.	

GUIDELINES & STRATEGIES	ADULT	LEARNER
		Ed is familiar with the routine, and knows he can pick whom he is to serve first.
	Sue guesses that Ed is thinking about whom to pick so she puts his thoughts into expression.	
Opportunity: Provide opportunities to interact	Sue **says**, "Who first?" while making an **empty hands gesture**, and **pointing** around the table.	
		Ed stands by Pat, a peer, with a tea cart that holds two pitchers of juice. One is a tan pitcher filled with apple juice and the other is a purple one filled with grape juice. Ed **points** to the pitchers to ask Pat what he wants.
	Pat **picks** the tan pitcher.	
Opportunity: Create need for requests	Sue **anticipates that Ed will ask for help, so she busies herself with another student** to give him an opportunity to try to get her attention.	
		Ed **looks** at Sue, but she does not see him. He **vocalizes**.
Sequencing: Encourage participation	Sue **looks up and responds**, "Yes, what?" and makes an **empty hands gesture** and a **quizzical expression**.	
		Ed makes a **pouring motion**, and **looks** at Sue.
Movement: Use (and respond to) movements as communicative behaviors *Nurturance: Provide support* *Opportunity: Provide opportunities to interact*	Sue **says**, "Oh, Ed needs Sue to help." Sue **makes the Sue gesture** and the **pouring motion**. She says, "OK!" Sue **guides Ed** to pour, using both hands. When finished, she **indicates** the juice and the group through **pointing and says**, "Pour juice for everybody." Sue makes a **pouring motion** when she says pour.	

GUIDELINES & STRATEGIES	ADULT	LEARNER
Opportunity: Provide opportunities to interact	She **says** to the group, "Ed pours the juice today." As she speaks, she **indicates Ed, makes a pouring motion,** and **indicates** the juice through **pointing.**	
		When Ed is giving Callie, another peer, a drink, Callie accidentally bumps his arm and a little juice falls on the table. Everyone **notices** it and **starts pointing and vocalizing** at the puddle.
♡ *Nurturance: Focus on individual's interest*	Sue **says**, "The juice spilled. Callie bumped Ed's arm and some juice spilled." As she speaks she **indicates Callie, makes a bumping motion, indicates Ed, and points to the puddle.** Sue directs Callie to clean up the mess while Ed finishes serving the other students.	
		When Ed has finished serving all the students their juice, he serves the popcorn.
Opportunity: Create need for requests	Sue **has arranged it so that he won't have enough bags of popcorn.**	
		When Ed runs out he goes to Sue, makes an eating motion and points to the table.
Sensitivity: Respond contingently	Sue **responds by getting more bags of popcorn.**	
Sensitivity: Respond to individual's level of communication	As the students are finishing, Sue directs everyone's attention to the blackboard by the snack area. Sue **says**, "Let's draw about snack." Sue makes a **drawing motion** when she says "draw" and **points** to the snack activity. She uses drawing with the students because she has found it's a good context for stimulating them to converse. In addition, the use of drawing broadens the range of topics that can be discussed because through drawings, events from the past and the future can	

GUIDELINES & STRATEGIES	ADULT	LEARNER
	be brought up without confusing the students.	
Sensitivity: Respond to individual's level of communication	Sue **says,** "Let's draw the juice spilling." She makes **pouring and spilling motions** to make sure everyone knows what she is going to draw. When they know what she is going to draw, they can suggest elements for her to include in the drawing. Sue picks the spilling to draw because everyone was attentive to it. Sue **puts her chalk** to the board and **pauses** to give the students an opportunity to communicate what to draw.	
Opportunity: Utilize time-delay		
		Ed points to Callie.
Sensitivity: Respond contingently	Sue **responds,** "Let's draw Callie."	
Opportunity: Provide choices	Sue **says,** "What now?" and **waits** with her chalk on the board for another suggestion. Pat suggests the puddle, Callie suggests the juice container, Ed suggests himself, and little by little the drawing is made.	
Opportunity: Provide opportunities to interact	Sue **says,** "What happened?" and **makes an empty hands gesture.**	
		Ed pantomimes being bumped.
Movement: Use (and respond to) movements as communicative behaviors	Sue **responds,** "Yes, Callie bumped Ed and the juice spilled," as she speaks she **indicates Callie** in the drawing, **makes a bumping motion, indicates Ed** in the drawing, and **points** to the place on the table where it happened. **Sue says,** "All right, finished with snack." She **makes the signal for finished.**	
	The children clean up their places with the help of the classroom aides.	
Sequencing: Establish routines	Sue indicates to Ed and another student, Jill, to wipe the table by **pointing** to each of them while making a **wiping motion** over the table. Sue **says,** "Wipe the table."	

GUIDELINES & STRATEGIES	ADULT	LEARNER
		Jill and Ed wipe the table as directed by the teacher. They are moving in time with each other. Ed looks up and smiles at Jill. Jill vocalizes to Ed. When the table is clean, Ed and Jill put their clothes away, and move on to their next activity.

ED DIALOGUE #2: Physical Education Session

Ed's program of physical education takes place with peers from different classrooms in the integrated public school he attends. Ten minutes before the group session, Ed has individual time with his instructor to work on specific motor skills and communication intervention that require more intensive instruction.

It is time for Ed's individual physical education session in the gym. Part of the gym activity is an obstacle course. Although the actual course is made of different sequences of obstacles and actions each day, the obstacle course is embedded in a sequence that does not change day-to-day. Kate, the Physical Education instructor, adheres to a routine so that Ed will know what to expect. This enables him to be relaxed because there are no surprises to catch him off guard or to confuse him. Also, because he knows what is going to happen, he can communicate about the upcoming steps in the sequence. In addition, Kate knows what Ed expects at each step so she can pair language and nonsymbolic communications with his expectations and, thus, help him to learn to understand more communication. Ed and Kate enter the gym walking side-by-side. Kate initiates arm swinging because she knows Ed likes to do it, and it encourages him to move both arms.

GUIDELINES & STRATEGIES	ADULT	LEARNER
	Ed knows the first step is to get the chairs. Kate put his expectations into expressions.	
Movement: Use movements as communicative behaviors Opportunity: Provide opportunities to interact	**She says,** "Get your chair," **makes a getting motion (i.e., pantomimes getting the chair), points** to the chair, and **points** to the obstacle course.	
		Ed gets a chair and starts pushing it toward the course.
Opportunity: Utilize time-delay	Kate **gets her chair,** but **pauses** to give Ed an opportunity to communicate with her.	
		Ed gets to the course and notices that Kate is not with him. He looks at Kate and points to the course.
Opportunity: Utilize time-delay	Kate **begins to move her chair,** but then **pauses** briefly to see if Ed will elaborate.	
		Ed makes a pushing motion and points to the course.
Sensitivity: Respond contingently Nurturance: Provide affection	Kate **responds** by **pushing her chair** next to his. She **looks at him, smiles, and pats him on the back.**	

182

GUIDELINES & STRATEGIES	ADULT	LEARNER
	She **says,** "My turn." She goes over to the first piece, which is a large cardboard tube turned so it's like a tunnel, and **makes a going through motion** with her hand. She **says,** "Go through." Then she goes to the second piece, a climbing gym, and **makes a climbing motion** with her hands. She says, "Climb over."	
Movement: Use movements as communicative behaviors		
		Ed starts to **gaze off.**
Sensitivity: Recognize individual's readiness for interaction	She **calls** "Ed," and **waves** her arms.	
		He looks.
Sensitivity: Recognize individual's readiness for interaction	Kate **continues moving but speaks a little louder and moves more emphatically to try to keep Ed's attention.** She goes on to the last piece, which is a bench about 6 inches off the ground. She makes a **walking motion with her hands** over the bench and **says,** "Walk." When she gets to the end of the bench, she makes a **jumping motion with her body, and says,** "Jump off." Then she goes through the obstacle course, repeating the words and motions before each action.	
Movement: Use movements as communicative behaviors		
Sequencing: Establish routines		
Sequencing: Provide turn-taking opportunities	She **points** to Ed and the obstacle course and **says,** "Your turn."	
		Ed is looking at the trampoline.
Nurturance: Expand on child-initiated behavior	Kate **responds,** "There's the trampoline." As she **speaks she points** to the trampoline and **makes a jumping motion** with her body.	
		Ed smiles.
Sequencing: Establish routines	Kate **returns to the routine saying,** "Your turn," and **pointing** to the course.	
		Ed goes through the course correctly until he gets to the bench. Then, he slides along the bench.
Movement: Respond to movements as communicative behaviors	Kate **goes over** and says, "Ed slides." She **slides her hand down the bench.**	

GUIDELINES & STRATEGIES	ADULT	LEARNER
Movement: Use movements as communicative behaviors	She **shakes her head,** and says, "Walk." She **makes the walking motion** with her hands.	
Movement: Select movements that accommodate the learner's ability to respond	The walking gesture does not seem to be registering with Ed. Kate decides to drop back to the lower level of demonstrating the act that she wants him to perform. She **walks** across the bench and has him imitate.	
		Ed imitates by walking down the bench.
Opportunity: Utilize time-delay	They repeat the obstacle several times until Kate is sure Ed knows the sequence. Then, after she explains the course, Kate **goes and stands by the tunnel and waits** to give Ed an opportunity to direct her through the activity using the motions she has been modeling for him.	
		Ed does not do anything.
Opportunity: Encourage participation	Kate **calls,** "Ed, what do I do?" She **makes an empty hands gesture** and **points** to the tunnel.	
		Ed makes the going through motion.
Sensitivity: Respond contingently	Kate **responds,** "Yes, go through!" She **goes through** the tunnel.	
Opportunity: Provide opportunities to interact	She looks at Ed and says, "What now?" She **makes the empty hands gesture** and **points** to the climbing gym.	
		Ed doesn't do anything.
Sequencing: Encourage participation	Kate **starts to go under** the climbing gym.	
		Ed jumps up, vocalizes, shakes his head, and makes the climbing motion.
Sensitivity: Respond contingently	Kate **smiles** broadly and **responds by coming back quickly** and **climbing over** the gym saying, "Climb," **making the climbing motion.**	

GUIDELINES & STRATEGIES	ADULT	LEARNER
Opportunity: Provide opportunities to interact	She **goes to the bench and says**, "What now?" She **makes the empty hands gesture** and **points** to the bench.	
		Ed makes the walking motion and the jumping motion.
Sensitivity: Respond contingently	Kate **responds** enthusiastically, "Yes, walk, walk, walk, walk, and jump off!" She **performs the actions** and the motions as she speaks.	
Sequencing: Establish routines *Nurturance: Provide affection*	She **returns to her chair and says**, "Finished," and **makes the finished signal.** She **smiles** at Ed and **tousles** his hair.	
		Ed smiles. **Ed is familiar with the sequence of the gym activity, so he is able to tell Kate what is next.** **He makes the drawing motion.**
Movement: Respond to movements as communicative behaviors	Kate **responds by nodding, making the drawing motion and pointing** to the obstacle course while **saying**, "Yes, drawing! We'll draw what we did." She uses pointing quite often with Ed to make sure that he is paying attention to the thing she is communicating about.	
		Ed stands up and pushes his chair to the table where they draw.
Opportunity: Create need for requests	Kate **doesn't come immediately.**	
		He see Kate is not coming. **He comes over and pulls her out of the chair by the arm, and makes the pushing motion.**
Sensitivity: Respond to individual's level of communication	Kate does not like it when Ed pulls on her, so she **responds** by modeling the expression she would like him to use. She	

GUIDELINES & STRATEGIES	ADULT	LEARNER
	says, "Ed says, 'Stand up,'" and **makes a standing up motion** with her hands and body.	
	She reminds herself that she ought to use this motion with Ed when she wants him to stand up, rather than pulling him up.	
Opportunity: Provide opportunities to interact	She **begins moving her chair,** but starts to go past the table.	
		Ed **vocalizes** and **points to the table.**
Sensitivity: Respond contingently	Kate **responds** by **coming back and sitting** at the table.	
Nurturance: Provide affection	She **smiles and pats** him.	
		Ed **smiles and watches her.**
Sequencing: Provide turn-taking opportunities	Kate **picks up the pen and says,** "What do we draw?" She **makes the drawing motion, the empty hands gesture,** and **points** to the paper.	
		Ed **points** to the tunnel, and **makes the going through motion.**
Movement: Respond to movements as communicative behaviors	Kate **responds by nodding, making the going through motion and saying,** "Yes, we went through the tunnel."	
Movement: Use movements as communicative behaviors	Kate **points** to the tunnel and **draws** it as Ed watches. Then **she says,** "Draw Ed going through the tunnel." She **makes the drawing motion, points** to Ed, and **makes the going through motion** as she speaks.	
Sequencing: Provide turn-taking opportunities	She **hands the pen** to Ed and **says,** "Your turn."	
	She always tries to get Ed to participate in the drawing because he is more attentive when he participates, and it helps him to understand the drawings.	
		Ed **draws a rough figure near the tunnel.**
Sequencing: Establish routines	As he draws, Kate **says,** "Ed went through the tunnel," **points** to Ed, and **makes the going through motion.** Then **she says,** "Finished," and **makes the finished signal.**	

GUIDELINES & STRATEGIES	ADULT	LEARNER

GUIDELINES & STRATEGIES **ADULT** **LEARNER**

Opportunity: Provide opportunities to interact

"What now?" She **makes the empty hands gesture** and **points** to a new page.

Ed **points** to the bench and makes the **walking** and **jumping** motions.

Movement: Respond to movements as communicative behaviors

Kate responds, "Yes, Ed walked on the bench and jumped off." She **makes the walking motion** when **she says,** "Walk," and **makes the jumping motion** when **she says,** "Jump."

Sequencing: Establish routines

Kate wants the drawings done in the same **sequence** they were done in to give Ed a sense of order.

Opportunity: Provide opportunities to interact

She **points** back to the course and **says,** "Ed went through the tunnel." She **points** to Ed, **makes the going through motion,** and **points** to the tunnel, "And then . . ." She **points** to the climbing gym. She **says,** "What now?" She **points** to the paper.

Ed makes the climbing motion and pushes Kate's hand.

Sensitivity: Respond to individual's level of communication

Nurturance: Expand on child-initiated behavior

Kate wants him to use the drawing motion rather than pushing her hand. Again, she **models the expression she would like him to use. She responds,** "Draw?" She **makes the drawing motion,** and **begins drawing** the climbing gym.

She does not ask him to imitate her expression because she does not want to encourage him to use communicative expressions when he has no communicative purpose. She would rather model the expression for him now, and encourage him to use it the next time he has a desire to communicate about drawing.

Sequencing: Provide turn-taking opportunities

Kate **draws** part of the climbing gym and then **hands the pen to Ed** to fill in the rungs on the ladder. She likes to give him practice drawing because the better he draws, the better a communicative medium it will be for him.

GUIDELINES & STRATEGIES	ADULT	LEARNER
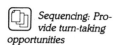 *Sequencing: Provide turn-taking opportunities*	She **says,** "Ed is drawing the ladder." She **makes the drawing motion,** and **points** to the ladder. She is always careful to point out the things they draw so that Ed will never lose sight of the fact that they are drawing real things.	
		Ed goes on to **draw himself.**
♡ *Nurturance: Focus on individual's interest*	Kate **responds,** "Who is that?" She **points** to herself, and she **points** to Ed.	
		Ed **points** to himself and **makes the climbing motion.**
☞ *Sensitivity: Respond to individual's level of communication*	Kate **responds,** "Oh, that's Ed, climbing." She **smiles and nods, points** to Ed, and **makes the climbing motion.** They go on to draw the picture of the activity on the bench. When they're finished, they push their chairs back to the obstacle course.	
Sequencing: Provide turn-taking opportunities *Opportunities: Provide choice*	Kate **says,** "Your turn," and **points** to Ed and to the obstacle course. She **goes to the course** with Ed and says, "Ball or tube?" as she **points to the big ball and the cardboard tube.**	
		Ed **points to the tube and pulls it up on its end. He pushes the ball away.**
Movement: Use movements matched to the level of the learner's actions *Opportunity: Provide choices*	Kate **says,** "You push the ball," while **making a pushing motion and pointing to the ball.** She says, "The climbing gym or the ladder?" as she **points** to the climbing gym and the ladder.	
		Ed **points to the climbing gym and makes the climbing motion.**
Opportunity: Provide choice	Kate **says,** "OK. Now, do you want the bench or the trampoline?" She **points to the bench and the trampoline.**	
		Ed **points to the trampoline and then pushes and pulls the bench out of the way.**

GUIDELINES & STRATEGIES	ADULT	LEARNER

 Nurturance: Provide support

"Look at Ed pull!" Kate **says** as she **makes a pulling motion.**

Kate is pleased to see him trying to use his weak arm to arrange the obstacle course.

Ed **climbs** into the tunnel, **crouches down,** and **pops out.** He **walks under** the climbing gym and, then, **goes** to the trampoline, **climbs up,** and **jumps.** He **comes back** to his chair.

 Opportunity: Utilize time-delay

 Opportunity: Provide opportunities to interact

Kate **waits** for him to signal her to start.

She anticipates that he will try to pull her out of her chair, so she discretely **moves her hands away** from him.

Ed **points** to the course, and **begins to reach** for her arm. When he doesn't see it right away, he makes the **stand up motion.**

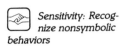 *Sensitivity: Recognize nonsymbolic behaviors*

 Nurturance: Provide support

Kate **responds** by **standing up** and **saying,** "Ed says, 'Stand up!'" She **makes the stand up motion** as she is talking. She **pats him** enthusiastically.

Ed **points** to the course.

Kate begins as before, explaining the course in simple language and gestures. As she goes through the course, she announces each movement before she does it in words and gestures. After they take turns repeating the sequence several times, Kate gets Ed to direct her through the course using pointing and gestures. When they are finished they go to the table and draw about it just as before.

ED DIALOGUE #3: Community Training

Ed is with some of his peers on a community training trip. The group has stopped to eat in a fast food restaurant. Ed steps up to the counter next to his teacher, Sue.

GUIDELINES & STRATEGIES	ADULT	LEARNER
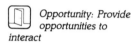 *Opportunity: Provide opportunities to interact*	"What do you want to eat?" says Sue as she **turns her palms up to make an empty hands gesture, makes an eating motion, and hands him a menu** containing pictures. A restaurant worker steps up to the counter. "May I take your order?"	
		Ed **vocalizes** and **points** to the picture of the french fries and cheeseburger.
	"You'd like a cheeseburger and french fries?" he asks.	
		Ed **smiles** and **points** to the picture of Coke.
Opportunity: Provide choices	"And a Coke. Anything else?"	
		Ed **does not respond.** He waits for his order. Ed is looking around excitedly, so he doesn't notice when his order comes.
Nurturance: Focus on individual's interest	"Ed, look," says Sue, as she **moves around in front of him** and **points** to his order. Sue always tries to get in front of Ed when she is trying to get his attention because she has noticed how many of her students do not like it when someone comes up behind them.	
		In his excitement, Ed turns around and reaches for his tray too quickly. He spills the Coke. He **takes Sue by the arm, points** to the menu overhead, **makes a drinking motion,** and **looks** at Sue.

GUIDELINES & STRATEGIES	ADULT	LEARNER
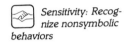 *Sensitivity: Recognize nonsymbolic behaviors*	Sue **responds,** "Yes, more Coke." She **nods, points** to the menu, and **makes a drinking motion.**	
Sequencing: Encourage participation	Then she **points** to the mess, **makes an empty hands gesture,** and says, "What do we do here?" She hopes Ed will answer with a communicative behavior.	
		Ed is familiar with messes and how to clean up, so he **makes a wiping motion.**
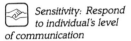 *Sensitivity: Respond to individual's level of communication*	Sue **responds,** "Yes, wipe up," and **makes the wiping motion.** "Get some napkins," she says, **making a taking out motion, pointing** to the napkin holder.	
		Ed gets a stack of napkins and pushes them toward Sue.
Nurturance: Create a positive setting for interactions	Sue **laughs** and responds, "No, you do it," and **pushes them back** to Ed.	
		Ed pushes them back to Sue.
Opportunity: Provide opportunities to interact	She compromises and takes half. She **says,** "Let's wipe up," **pointing** to Ed and herself, and then **making the wiping motion.**	
	She remembers that she used to have to perform the real wiping action for Ed in order for him to understand her. Now he responds to the motion she makes without a sponge or cloth in her hand.	
Opportunity: Utilize time-delay	She **picks up** the napkins and **waits** for him to begin, because she knows if she starts first, he will just watch her do it.	
		Ed starts wiping up the mess and Sue joins him. He is moving very slowly and not very effectively.
	She could just put her hand over his hand and manipulate him to do it better and faster. She has found that she can get learners to participate in other ways and, in general, tries not to use physical manipulation.	

GUIDELINES & STRATEGIES	ADULT	LEARNER
Sensitivity: Recognize individual's readiness for interaction	She **initiates a game of chasing his hand** and bumping into him to get him to move a little faster.	
Nurturance: Create a positive setting for interactions	Sue **looks at Ed,** smiles, and **says,** "Here I come to get you. Gotcha." **She bumps his hand.**	
		Ed smiles and moves his napkin away from her.
Sequencing: Utilize patterns in games	Sue **smiles and says,** "Here I come to get you. Gotcha, gotcha, gotcha." She **bumps his hand quickly.**	
		Ed smiles and moves his napkin away. They continue in the same way for several exchanges.
		Ed perks up and soon he finishes the job.
Opportunity: Provide opportunities to interact	Sue **points** to the pile of dirty napkins and says, "What now?" She wants him to answer with a communicative behavior.	
		Ed picks up the napkins and thrusts them toward the waste bin.
		He looks back to Sue for confirmation.
Sensitivity: Recognize nonsymbolic behavior (and) Respond contingently	She **smiles and responds,** "Throw them away. Good." She **makes a throwing motion** when she says, "Throw."	
		Ed throws the napkins away. He comes back holding his dirty hands away from his body and grimacing.
Sensitivity: Recognize nonsymbolic behaviors	Sue **responds** by putting Ed's feelings into words and gestures. "Ed wants to wash up," she says, as she **makes a hand washing motion,** and **points** to the bathroom.	
		Ed goes to wash up.
Opportunity: Create need for requests	While Ed is gone his Coke comes. Sue **does not get catsup, a straw, or napkins for Ed** to see if he will ask for these items.	

GUIDELINES & STRATEGIES	ADULT	LEARNER
		When Ed gets back, he carefully puts the new Coke on his tray.
		Ed **notices** that he does not have catsup. He **looks** at Sue and **pantomimes** dipping his fries and **points** to the place on his tray where the catsup should go.
Sensitivity: Recognize nonsymbolic behaviors	Sue **responds** by **getting the catsup** and **saying,** "You need catsup."	
		Ed **pantomimes** drinking through a straw and **pulls Sue** to where the straws are kept.
Nurturance: Expand on child-initiated behaviors	Sue **responds by going with him and copying his motion.**	
		Ed gets a straw and picks up some napkins.
Sensitivity: Respond contingently	Sue **says,** "You got napkins," and **makes a face wiping motion.**	
Nurturance: Provide affection	She **says,** "Good, Ed," and **pats him.** Sue goes back to carry a tray for another student and walks back toward Ed.	
		He takes Sue's arm, makes a carrying motion, and points to his tray.
Sensitivity: Recognize nonsymbolic behaviors	Sue shows him her hands are already full. She **shakes her head** and **makes an "I'm sorry" face.**	
Opportunity: Provide opportunities to interact	She can see Ed is getting frustrated. She responds quickly because she doesn't want him to fall apart. She frees one of her hands long enough to **point** to Phil, Ed's favorite paraprofessional.	

GUIDELINES & STRATEGIES	ADULT	LEARNER
		Ed goes to where Phil is sitting, **pulls Phil up**, **points** to his tray, and **makes a carrying motion**.
♡ *Nurturance: Expand on child-initiated behavior*	Phil doesn't like it when Ed pulls on him, so he models the expression he would rather have Ed use under the circumstances. **He says,** "Ed says, 'Phil,'" and he **makes the beard stroking motion** Ed uses to represent Phil. "Carry my tray." As he speaks he **makes a carrying motion** and **points** to the tray.	
		Ed **nods**.
	Phil **responds**, "OK," and **nods**.	
⬜ *Opportunity: Utilize time-delay*	Phil returns with the tray and **waits** for Ed to indicate where to put it.	
		Ed **points** to the table where Phil and one of Ed's buddies, Paul, are sitting.
♡ *Nurturance: Provide affection*	Phil puts the tray down at the table to which Ed pointed. He **pats** Ed as he sits down next to him.	
⬛ *Movement: Use movements as communicative behaviors*	Phil **says**, "We're going to play video games when we're finished." He **points** to Paul and himself and then to the video games.	
		Ed **misunderstands and get up to go to the video game area.**
♡ *Nurturance: Focus on individual's interest*	Phil **steps in front of him** and **says**, "No. Eat, now." He **points** to Ed and **makes an eating motion.**	
		Ed goes back to **sit down**. He begins eating. He can't open his catsup so he **hands it** to Phil, **makes a squeezing motion**, and **points** to where he wants it on the plate.

GUIDELINES & STRATEGIES	ADULT	LEARNER

 Sensitivity: Respond contingently

Phil **responds by opening** the catsup.

During lunch, Ed **gazes** at the lights, **laughs**, shakes his head, and **rocks** fast enough to shake the table.

 Sensitivity: Respond to individual's level of communication

Phil wants to stop Ed from behaving this way as unobtrusively as possible. He **slips his arm around Ed's shoulders** from time to time to prevent him from rocking.

Opportunity: Provide opportunities to interact

After they finish eating, Phil **takes his tray and dumps his trash** in the waste bin. He **looks back** at Paul and Ed.

Phil has noticed that there are a lot of students with whom he works who never seem to act on their own. They sit and wait to be told what to do. He wonders if he encourages that by always telling them what to do. Lately, he's been trying not to tell them every move to make. Sometimes, like now, he just gives them a hint and gives them some time to act on their own.

Paul is familiar with clean up because this is a routine activity at school. He recognizes Phil's cue and responds by **dumping his trash,** too. As Paul dumps his trash, **Phil says,** "That's right! Clean your tray," **makes a cleaning motion,** and **points** to the tray. He **pats** Paul on the back. He **looks back** at Ed.

Nurturance: Provide support

Ed **follows** Paul's lead and **comes over** and **dumps his trash** in the waste bin.

 Sensitivity: Respond to individual's level of communication

Nurturance: Provide affection

Phil **responds,** "Ed, you clean your tray," **makes the cleaning motion,** and **points** to the tray. He **pats** Ed on the back.

Phil has been making an effort lately to use communication to describe what the students are doing. He had caught himself only communicating when he wanted the students to do things.

GUIDELINES & STRATEGIES	ADULT	LEARNER

Now he realizes that he was only exposing the students to one purpose for communicating: to make requests. Now he knows that when he uses descriptions he is exposing them to another form of communication that is used—conveying information through describing.

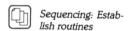 *Nurturance: Focus on individual's interest*

Phil says, "Let's go play," and **points to the video games.**

They go to the video area. Both Ed and Paul are attracted to the same game.

Opportunity: Provide opportunities to interact

Phil **comes over and says,** "This one?" He **points** to the game.

Ed is familiar with video games. He **points** to the slot and **extends his hand** for a quarter. Ed puts the quarter in the machine and **smiles** excitedly when the lights and music come on. He pushes the buttons and watches the figures move around. When it's over, he **extends his** hand for another quarter.

Sequencing: Establish routines

Phil **responds,** "No, we're finished now," and **makes the finished sign.** He **says,** "Time to go," and **points** to the door.

◄ APPENDIX ►

Format for Developing Nonsymbolic Intervention Strategies

Description of Learner

_____

_____

_____

_____

_____

_____

_____

Purposes for Learner's Communication Intervention

Developing Nurturance

_____

_____

_____

_____

Enhancing Sensitivity

_____

_____

_____

_____

Increasing Opportunities

_____

_____

_____

_____

_____

Sequencing Experiences

_____

_____

_____

_____

_____

Utilizing Movement

_____

_____

_____

_____

_____

Glossary

Anticipation Shelf   A communication strategy that: 1) displays/uses an arrangement of objects or pictures to inform the learner of upcoming activities, and 2) is used as a context and method for conveying information to the learner.

Communication   A social interaction that exchanges information, ideas, desires, requests, or questions. The transmission and reception of the message may use symbolic behaviors (e.g., spoken word, written word, sign language, Blissymbolics) or nonsymbolic behaviors (e.g., facial expression, body movement, touch, gesture).

Dyad   Refers to the partnership that is exhibited as two people participate in communicative exchanges (see reciprocal); Considered as one unit.

Expressive Communication   Conveying, sending, or transmitting a message through symbolic or nonsymbolic means.

Functionality   The integration of useful and relevant communication training that is directly applicable to the individual's daily life situation.

Intentional Communication   An expression or behavior that is planned, deliberate, and purposeful.

Language   Communication by the use of a learned, arbitrary symbolic system. There are rules that govern the order and sequence of the symbols of any language. (see Symbolic)

Movement   An intervention procedure referring to part of the van Dijk theory of adult and child participating in reciprocal exchanges through the mutual physical movements of their bodies. The use of movement encourages communication by developing the individual's: 1) awareness of self, 2) separation of self from the environment; and 3) recognition of others as responsive, social partners.

Natural Context   The use of naturally arising events within an everyday setting to integrate communication training that is appropriate and relevant to the needs of the individual.

Nonintentional Act   Any behavior performed without intention, plan, or purpose.

Nonintentional Communication   Expressing a nonintentional act that is not planned, deliberate, or purposeful but is interpreted as a communicative message.

Nonsymbolic   The use of gesture, facial expression, body movement, eye gaze, vocal sounds, and other expressions that are not part of symbolic communicative systems.

Nurturance   Emotional warmth and caring that fosters a supportive atmosphere. Nurturance helps to create a positive relationship that promotes interest in communicative interactions, and ensures a willingness to participate in social exchange.

Opportunity   A favorable situation for communicative exchanges to occur that encourages involvement, participation, and a reason to communicate.

Receptive Communication   The process of receiving and understanding a message.

Reciprocal Interaction   Communication that involves mutual exchanges between two people as they alternate between giving and receiving communicative messages.

Reciprocity   The give and take nature of communication exchanges and bi-directional influences of communicators on each other. Communicators have dual roles as both initiators and responders.

Responsiveness   The ability to perceive and interpret nonsymbolic behaviors in a sensitive fashion that is appropriate and satisfying to the individual who uses nonsymbolic communication. Responsiveness facilitates early communicative behavior by promoting an awareness of another person as an important agent in social interactions.

Sensitivity   An acute awareness of the needs and emotions of others, involving high responsivity to the subtle cues of others. Nonsymbolic communication is facilitated when sensitivity is used to perceive and interpret these behaviors.

Sequence   A related continuous series of activities using an organized framework that establishes regularized formats. Utilizing ordered sequences increases the individual's familiarity with interactions that facilitate communication by promoting active participation in social exchanges.

Symbolic   The use of abstract or conventional signs that represent elements, relations, or qualities (e.g., written words, spoken words, sign language, Blissymbolics, braille).

References

Adamson, L.B., & Bakeman, R. (1984). Mother's communicative acts: Changes during infancy. *Infant Behavior and Development, 7*, 467–478.

Affleck, G., McGrade, B.J., McQueeney, M., & Allen, D. (1982). Promise of relationship-focused early intervention in developmental disabilities. *The Journal of Special Education, 16* (4), 413–430.

Alpert, C. (1984). *Training parents to use incidental teaching as a means of improving the communication skills of their language-delayed children.* Unpublished doctoral dissertation. University of Kansas, Lawrence.

Anderson, S.R., & Spradlin, J.E. (1980). The generalized effects of productive labeling training involving comment object classes. *Journal of The Association of the Severely Handicapped, 5*, 143–157.

Bakeman, R., & Adamson, L. B. (1984). Coordinating attention to people and objects in mother-infant and peer-infant interactions. *Child Development, 55*, 1278–1289.

Bakeman, R., & Brown, J. V. (1977). Behavioral dialogues: An approach to the assessment of mother-infant interaction. *Child Development, 48* (10), 195–203.

Barnard, K., Bee, H.L., & Hammond, M.A. (1984). Developmental changes in maternal interactions with term and preterm infants. *Infant Behavior and Development, 7*, 101–113.

Bates, E. (1976). *Language and context: The acquisition of pragmatics.* New York: Academic Press.

Bates, E., Benigni, L., Bretherton, I., Camaioni, L., & Volterra, V. (1979). *The emergence of symbols.* New York: Academic Press.

Bates, E., Bretherton, I., Beeghly-Smith, M., & McNew, S. (1982). Social bases of language development: A reassessment. In H.W. Reese & L.P. Lipseitt (Eds.), *Advances in child development and behavior* (pp. 7–75). New York: Academic Press.

Bates, E., Camaioni, L., & Volterra, V. (1975). The acquisition of performatives prior to speech. *Merrill-Palmer Quarterly, 21*, 205–226.

Bell, S. M., & Ainsworth, M. D. S. (1972). Infant crying and maternal responsiveness. *Child Development, 43*, 1171–1180.

Bloom, L., & Lahey, M. (1978). *Language development and language disorders.* New York: John Wiley & Sons.

Bricker, D.D., & Carlson, L. (1981). Issues in early language intervention. In R.L. Schiefelbusch & D.D. Bricker (Eds.), *Early language: Acquisition and intervention* (Vol. VI, pp. 477–515). Baltimore: University Park Press.

Bricker, D., & Dennison, L. (1978). Training prerequisites to verbal behavior. In M. Snell (Ed.), *Systematic instruction of the moderately and severely handicapped,* (pp. 157–178). Columbus: Charles E. Merrill.

Brown, F., Evans, I.M., Weed, K., & Owen, V. (1986). *Making functional skills functional: A component model.* Unpublished manuscript, State University of New York, Binghamton.

Brown, F., Holvoet, J., Guess, D., & Mulligan, M. (1980). The individualized curriculum sequencing model (III): Small group instruction. *Journal of The Association for the Severely Handicapped, 5*, 352–367.

Bruner, J.S. (1975). From communication to language: A psychological perspective. *Cognition, 3*, 255–287.

Bruner, J.S. (1975). The ontogenesis of speech acts. *Journal of Child Language, 2*, 1–19.

Bruner, J.S. (1977). Early social interaction and language acquisition. In H.R. Schaffer (Ed.), *Studies in mother-infant interaction* (pp. 271–289). New York: Academic Press.

Bullis, M. (Ed.). (1985). *Communication development in young children with deaf-blindness: Literature Review 1.* Monmouth, OR: Communication Skills Center for Young Children with Deaf-Blindness, Teaching Research.

Bullis, M. (Ed.). (1986). *Communication development in young children with deaf-blindness: Literature Review II.* Monmouth, OR: Communication Skills Center for Young Children with Deaf-Blindness, Teaching Research.

Bullis, M. (Ed.). (1987). *Communication development in young children with deaf-blindness: Literature Review III.* Monmouth, OR: Communication Skills Center for Young Children with Deaf-Blindness, Teaching Research.

Bullis, M. (Ed.). (1989). *Communication development in young children with deaf-blindness: Literature Review IV.* Monmouth, OR: Communication Skills Center for Young Children with Deaf-Blindness, Teaching Research.

Carlson, L., & Bricker, D.D. (1982). Dyadic and contingent aspects of early communicative intervention. In D. Bricker (Ed.), *Intervention with at risk and handicapped infants: From research to application* (pp. 291–308). Baltimore: University Park Press.

Clark, G.N., & Seifer, R. (1983). Facilitating mother-infant communication: A treatment model for high-risk and developmentally-delayed infants. *Infant Mental Health Journal, 4* (2), 67–81.

Collis, G.M., & Schaffer, H.R. (1975). Synchronization of visual attention in mother-infant pairs. *Journal of Child Psychology and Psychiatry, 16*, 315–320.

Crnic, K.A., Ragozin, A.S., Greenberg, M.T., Robinson, N.M., & Basham, R.B. (1983). Social interaction and developmental competence of preterm and full-term infants during the first year of life. *Child Development, 54*, 1199–1210.

Donnellan, A.M., Mirenda, P.L., Mesaros, R.A., & Fassbender, L.L. (1984). Analyzing the communicative functions of aberrant behavior. *Journal of The Association for Persons with Severe Handicaps, 9* (3), 201–212.

Dunst, C.J., & Lesko, J.J., Holbert, K.A., Wilson, L.L., Sharpe, K.L., & Liles, R.F. (1987). A systematic approach to infant intervention. *Topics in Early Childhood Special Education, 7*(2), 19–37.

Field, T. (1983). High-risk infants "have less fun" during early interactions. *Topics in Early Childhood Special Education, 3*(1), 77–87.

Folger, J., & Chapman, R.S. (1978). A pragmatic analysis of spontaneous imitations. *Journal of Child Language, 5*, 25–38.

Gaylord-Ross, R., Stremel-Campbell, K., & Storey, K. (1986). Social skill training in natural contexts. In R.H. Horner, L.H. Meyer, & H.D.B. Fredericks (Eds.), *Education of learners with severe handicaps: Exemplary service strategies* (pp. 161–187). Baltimore: Paul H. Brookes Publishing Co.

Goetz, L., & Sailor, W. (1988). New directions: Communication development in persons with severe disabilities. *Topics in Language Disorders, 8*(4), 41–54.

Guess, D., Benson, H., & Siegel-Causey, E. (1985). Concepts and issues related to choice-making and autonomy among persons with severe handicaps. *Journal for The Association for Persons with Severe Handicaps, 10* (2), 79–86.

Guess, D., Horner, D., Utley, B., Holvoet, J., Maxon, D., Tucker, D., & Warren, S. (1978). A functional curriculum sequencing model for teaching the severely handicapped. *AAESPH Review, 3*, 202–215.

Guess, D., & Siegel-Causey, E. (1985). Behavioral control and education of severely handicapped students: Who's doing what to whom? and why? In D. Bricker & J. Filler (Eds.), *Severe mental retardation: From theory to practice* (pp. 230–244). Reston, VA: Council for Exceptional Children.

Halle, J. (1982). Teaching functional language to the handicapped: An integrative model of natural environment teaching techniques. *Journal of The Association for the Severely Handicapped, 7*(4), 29–37.

Halle, J. (1984). Arranging the natural environment to occasion language: Giving severely language-delayed children reason to communicate. *Seminars in Speech and Language, 5* (3), 185–197.

Halle, J. (1985). Enhancing social competence through language: An experimental analysis of a practical procedure for teachers. *Topics in Early Childhood Special Education, 4* (4), 77–92.

Hammer, E. (1982). The development of language in the deaf-blind multihandicapped child: Progression of instructional methods. In E. Shroyer & D. Tweedie (Eds.), *The multihandicapped hearing impaired child* (pp. 193–200). Washington, DC: Gallaudet College.

Harrell, R.L., & Strauss, F.A. (1986). Approaches to increasing assertive behavior and communication skills in blind and visually impaired persons. *Journal of Visual Impairment and Blindness, 24* (6), 794–798.

Hart, B., & Risley, T.R. (1975). Incidental teaching of language in the preschool. *Journal of Applied Behavior Analysis, 8*, 411–420.

Helmstetter, E., & Guess, D. (1987). Application of the individualized curriculum sequencing model to learners with severe sensory impairments. In L. Goetz, D. Guess, & K. Stremel-Campbell (Eds.), *Innovative program design for individuals with dual sensory impairments* (pp. 255–282). Baltimore: Paul H. Brookes Publishing Co.

Hodapp, R.M., & Goldfield, E.C. (1983). The use of mother-infant games with delayed children. *Early Child Development and Care, 13*(1), 17–32.

Holvoet, J., Guess, D., Mulligan, M., & Brown, F. (1980). The individualized curriculum sequencing model (II): A teaching strategy for severely handicapped students. *Journal of the Association for the Severely Handicapped, 5*, 337–351.

Holvoet, J., Mulligan, M., Schussler, N., Lacy, L., & Guess, D. (1984). *The Kansas individualized curriculum sequencing model.* Portland: Applied Systems Instruction, Evaluation, and Publishing (ASIEP).

Houghton, J., Bronicki, G.J., & Guess, D. (1987). Opportunities to express preferences and make choices among students with severe disabilities in classroom settings. *Journal of the Association for Persons with Severe Handicaps, 12* (1), 18–27.

James, S.D., & Egel, A.L. (1986). A direct prompting strategy for increasing reciprocal interactions between handicapped and nonhandicapped siblings. *Journal of Applied Behavior Analysis, 19*, 173–186.

Kaiser, A.P., Alpert, C.L., & Warren, S.L. (1987). Teaching functional language: Strategies for intervention. In M.E. Snell (Ed.), *Systematic instruction of persons with severe handicaps,* (pp. 247–272). Columbus, OH: Charles E. Merrill.

Kaye, K. (1982). *The mental and social life of babies.* Chicago: University of Chicago Press.

Kent-Udolf, L. (1984). Current therapy of communication disorders: Programming language. In W. Perkins (Ed.), *Language handicaps in children* (pp. 15–25). New York: Thieme-Stratton, Inc.

Klein, M.D., & Briggs, M.H. (1987). Facilitating mother-infant communicative interaction in mothers of high-risk infants. *Journal of Childhood Communication Disorders, 10*(2), 95–106.

Kogan, K., Tyler, N., & Turner, P. (1974). The process of interpersonal adaptations between mothers and their cerebral palsied children. *Developmental Medicine and Child Neurology, 16*, 518–527.

Levin, H., Snow, C., & Lee, K. (1984). Nurturant talk to children. *Language and Speech, 27* (Part 2), 147–162.

Lewis, M., & Goldberg, S. (1969). Perceptual-cognitive development in infancy: A generalized expectancy model as a function of the mother-infant interaction. *Merrill-Palmer Quarterly, 15*, 81–100.

Liberty, K.A., Haring, N.G., & Martin, M.M. (1981). Teaching new skills to the severely handicapped. *Journal of The Association for the Severely Handicapped, 6* (1), 5–13.

MacDonald, J.D. (1985). Language through conversion: A model for intervention with language delayed persons. In S.F. Warren & A.K. Rogers-Warren (Eds.), *Teaching functional language* (pp. 89–122). Baltimore: University Park Press.

Mittler, P., & Berry, P. (1977). Demanding language. In P. Mittler (Ed.), *Research to practice in mental retardation: Education and training* (Vol. II, pp. 245–252). International Association for Scientific Study in Mental Deficiency.

Mount, M., & Shea, V. (1982). *How to recognize and assess pre-language skills in the severely handicapped.* Lawrence, KS: H. & H. Enterprises.

Mulligan, M., Guess, D., Holvoet, J., & Brown, F. (1980). The individualized curriculum sequencing model (I): Implications from research on massed, distributed, or spaced trial learning. *Journal of The Association for the Severely Handicapped, 5*, 325–336.

Musselwhite, C.R. (1986). *Adaptive play for special needs children: Strategies to enhance communication and learning.* San Diego, CA: College-Hill Press.

Musselwhite, C.R., & St. Louis, K.W. (1988). *Communication programming for persons with severe handicaps: Vocal and augmentative strategies.* San Diego, CA: College-Hill Press.

Newson, J. (1977). An intersubjective approach to the systematic description of mother-infant interaction. In H.R. Schaffer (Ed.), *Studies in mother-infant interaction* (pp. 47–61). New York: Academic Press.

Newson, J. (1979). The growth of shared understandings between infant and caregiver. In M. Bullowa (Ed.), *Before speech: The beginning of interpersonal communication* (pp. 207–222). London: Cambridge University Press.

Newson, J., Gregory, S., & Hartley, G. (1985). *Teasing and teaching.* Unpublished manuscript, The University of Nottingham, Nottingham, England.

Odom, S.L. (1983). The development of social interchanges in infancy. In S.G. Garwood & R.R. Fewell (Eds.), *Educating handicapped infants: Issues in development and intervention* (pp. 215–254). Rockville, MD: Aspen Publishers Inc.

Peck, C.A. (1985). Increasing opportunities for social control by children with autism and severe handicaps: Effects on student behavior and perceived classroom climate. *Journal of The Association for Persons with Severe Handicaps, 10* (4), 183–193.

Peck, C., & Schuler, A.L. (1987). Assessment of social/communicative behavior for students with autism and severe handicaps: The importance of asking the right question. In T. Layton (Ed.), *Language and treatment of autistic and developmentally disordered children.* Springfield, IL: Charles C Thomas.

Reichle, J., & Keogh, W.J. (1986). Communication instruction for learners with severe handicaps. Some unresolved issues. In R.H. Horner, L.H. Meyer, & H.D.B. Fredericks (Eds.), *Education of learners with severe handicaps: Exemplary service strategies* (pp. 189–219). Baltimore: Paul H. Brookes Publishing Co.

Rogow, S.M. (1984). The uses of social routines to facilitate communication in visually impaired and multihandicapped children. *Topics in Early Childhood Special Education, 3* (4), 64–70.

Rowland, C., & Schweigert, P. (1988). *Tangible symbol systems. Symbolic communication for individuals with multisensory impairments.* Eugene: Oregon Research Institute.

Rowland, C., & Stremel-Campbell, K. (1987). Share and share alike: Conventional gestures to emergent language for learners with sensory impairments. In L. Goetz, D. Guess, & K. Stremel-Campbell (Eds.), *Innovative program design for individuals with dual sensory impairments* (pp. 49–75). Baltimore: Paul H. Brookes Publishing Co.

Sachs, J. (1984). Children's play and communicative development. In R.L. Schiefelbusch & J. Pickar (Eds.), *The acquisition of communicative competence* (pp. 109–135). Baltimore: University Park Press.

Sailor, W., & Guess, D. (1983). *Severely handicapped students: An instructional design.* Boston: Houghton Mifflin.

Schaffer, H.R. (Ed.) (1977). *Studies in mother-infant interaction.* New York: Academic Press.

Schiefelbusch, R.L. (1984). Speech, language, and communication disorders of the multiply handicapped. *Folia Phoniatrica, 36* (1), 8–23.

Schuler, A.L., & Prizant, B.M. (1987). Facilitating communication: Prelanguage approaches. In D.J. Cohen & A.M. Donnellon (Eds.), *Handbook of autism and atypical developmental disorders* (pp. 301–315). New York: John Wiley & Sons.

Schweigert, P. (1987). Contingency intervention. In M. Bullis (Ed.), *Communication development in young children with deaf-blindness: Literature review III* (pp. 185–204). Monmouth, OR: Deaf-Blind Communication Skills Center.

Seligman, M. (1975). *Helplessness: On depression, development, and death.* San Francisco: W.H. Freeman.

Shevin, M., & Klein, N. (1984). The importance of choice-making skills for students with severe disabilities. *Journal of The Association for Persons with Severe Handicaps, 9* (3), 159–166.

Siegel-Causey, E., & Downing, J. (1987). Nonsymbolic communication development: Theoretical concepts and educational strategies. In L. Goetz, D. Guess, & K. Stremel-Campbell (Eds.), *Innovative program design for individuals with dual sensory impairments* (pp. 15–48). Baltimore: Paul H. Brookes Publishing Co.

Siegel-Causey, E., Ernst, B., & Guess, D. (1989). Nonsymbolic communication in early interactional processes and implications for intervention. In M. Bullis (Ed.), *Communication development in young children with deaf-blindness: Literature Review IV* (pp. 69–122). Monmouth, OR: Deaf-Blind Communication Skills Center.

Siegel-Causey, E., Ernst, B., & Guess, D. (1987). Elements of nonsymbolic communication and early interactional processes. In M. Bullis (Ed.), *Communication development in young children with deaf-blindness: Literature Review III* (pp. 57–102). Monmouth, OR: Deaf-Blind Communication Skills Center.

Siegel-Causey, E., & Guess, D. (1985). Early development of prelinguistic communication. In M. Bullis (Ed.), *Communication development in young children with deaf-blindness: Literature Review I* (pp. 61–77). Monmouth, OR: Deaf-Blind Communication Skills Center.

Siegel-Causey, E., Sims, C., Ernst, B., & Guess, D. (1986). Elements of prelanguage communication and early interactional processes. In M. Bullis (Ed.), *Communication development in young children with deaf-blindness: Literature Review II* (pp. 59–83). Monmouth, OR: Deaf-Blind Communication Skills Center.

Snow, C.E. (1984). Parent-child interaction and the development of communicative ability. In R.L. Schiefelbusch & J. Pickar (Eds.), *The acquisition of communicative competence* (pp. 69–107). Baltimore: University Park Press.

Stern, D. (1974). Mother and infant at play: The dyadic interaction involving facial, vocal, and gaze behaviors. In M. Lewis & R. Rosenblum (Eds.), *The effect of the infant on its caregiver,* (pp. 187–213). New York: John Wiley & Sons.

Stern, D.N. (1977). *The first relationship: Infant and mother.* London: Fontana/Open Books.

Stillman, R.D., & Battle, C.W. (1984). Developing prelanguage communication in the severely handicapped: An interpretation of the van Dijk method. *Seminars in Speech and Language, 5* (3), 159–170.

Stillman, R.D., & Battle, C.W. (1986a). *Categories of communicative intentions.* Unpublished manuscript, University of Texas, Callier Center for Communication Disorders, Dallas.

Stillman, R.D., & Battle, C.W. (1986b, November). *Communicative expressions directed toward students having multiple handicaps.* Paper presented at the Annual Meeting of the Association for Persons with Severe Handicaps, San Francisco, CA.

Stillman, R.D., & Battle, C.W. (1986c). Developmental assessment of communicative abilities in the deaf-blind. In D. Ellis (Ed.), *Sensory impairments in mentally handicapped people* (pp. 319–335). London: Croom Helm.

Stillman, R.D., & Battle, C.W. (1986d). *Procedures for the assessment of focus and intentions of communicative expressions directed toward persons having multiple handicaps.* Unpublished manuscript, University of Texas, Dallas.

Stremel-Campbell, K., & Rowland, C. (1987). Prelinguistic communication intervention: Birth-to-2. *Topics in Early Childhood Special Education, 7*(2), 49–58.

Touchette, P.E., & Schwartz, J. (1975). *The "delay" procedure, some preliminary instructions.* Unpublished manuscript, Eunice Kennedy Shriver Center, Waltham, MA.

Tyler, N.B., & Kogan, K.L. (1977). Reduction of stress between mothers and their handicapped children. *The American Journal of Occupational Therapy, 31,* 151–155.

van Dijk, J. (1965a). The first steps of the deaf-blind children towards language. *Proceedings of the Conference on the Deaf-Blind,* Refsnes, Denmark (pp. 47–50). Boston: Perkins School for the Blind.

van Dijk, J. (1965b). Motor development in the education of deaf-blind children. *Proceedings of the Conference on the Deaf-Blind,* Refsnes, Denmark (pp. 41–47). Boston: Perkins School for the Blind.

van Dijk, J. (1966). The first steps of the deaf-blind children towards language. *The International Journal for the Education of the Blind, 15* (4), 112–114.

van Dijk, J. (1967). The non-verbal deaf-blind child and his world: His outgrowth toward the world of symbols. *Proceedings of the Jaarverslag Institute voor Doven, 1964–1967* (pp. 73–110). Sint-Michielsgestel, Holland.

van Dijk, J. (1986). An educational curriculum for deaf-blind multi-handicapped persons. In D. Ellis (Ed.), *Sensory impairments in mentally handicapped people* (pp. 375–382). London: Croom-Helm.

Walker, J.A., & Kershman, S.M. (1981, April). *Deaf-blind babies in social interaction: Questions of maternal adaptation.* Paper presented at the meeting ot the Society for Research in Child Development, Boston, MA.

Walker, J.A., Levine, M.H., & Grasse, D.M. (1982). Maternal language in teaching and play interactions with handicapped babies. *Journal of the Division for Early Childhood, 5,* 86–96.

Warren, S.F., & Rogers-Warren, A.K. (Eds.). (1985). *Teaching functional language: Generalization and maintenance of language skills.* Baltimore: University Park Press.

Werner, H., & Kaplan, B. (1963). *Symbol formation.* New York: John Wiley & Sons.

Writer, J. (1987). A movement-based approach to the education of students who are sensory impaired/multihandicapped. In L. Goetz, D. Guess, & K. Stremel-Campbell (Eds.), *Innovative program design for individuals with dual sensory impairments* (pp. 191–223). Baltimore: Paul H. Brookes Publishing Co.

Yoder, D.E., & Kraat, A. (1983). Intervention issues in nonspeech communication. *American Speech-Language-Hearing Association Reports, 12,* 27–51.

Yoder, D., & Reichle, J. (1977). Some current perspectives on teaching communication functions to mentally retarded children. In P. Mittler (Ed.), *Research to practice in mental retardation, education, and training, Volume II* (pp. 199–205). Baltimore: University Park Press.

Index